ADVERTISING
Antiques

While every care has been taken in the compiling of information contained in this volume, the publisher cannot accept liability for loss, financial or otherwise, incurred by reliance placed on the information herein.

The publishers wish to express their sincere thanks to the following for their involvement and assistance in the production of this volume:

Editor: Tony Curtis
Photographer: Phillip Springthorpe
Foreword: Eelin McIvor
Editorial: Annette Curtis
                 Catriona Day
                 Donna Cruickshank
                 Angela De Marco
                 Donna Rutherford
                 Jacqueline Leddy
                 James Brown
                 Nicky Fairburn
                 Frank Burrell
                 Tim Barnard (Airbrush Retoucher)

A CIP catalogue record for this book is available from the British Library.

ISBN 86248-147-3

Copyright © Lyle Publications MCMXCIII
Glenmayne, Galashiels, Scotland

Typeset by Word Power, Coldingham, Berwickshire.
Printed and bound in Great Britain by
Butler & Tanner Ltd., Frome and London.

ADVERTISING
Antiques

TONY CURTIS

Auction Team Köln, Postfach 50 11 68, D-5000 Köln 50, Germany.
Brian Bates, Fairview, Maer, Newcastle, Staffs.
Jim Binns, 38a High Street, Kington, Herefordshire.
Christie's Scotland, 164-166 Bath Street, Glasgow G2 4TG.
Christie's South Kensington Ltd., 85 Old Brompton Road, London SW7 3LD.
Christie's, 8 King Street, London SW1Y 6QT.
Christie's East, 219 East 67th Street, New York, NY 10021, USA.
Nic Costa, 166 Camden Street, London NW1 9PT.
George Court, 48a Bridge Street, Leominster, Herts HR6 8DZ.
Finarte, 20121 Milano, Piazzetta Bossi 4, Italy.
Muir Hewitt, Halifax Antiques Centre, Queen Road, Halifax HX1 4LR.
Dave Lewis, 20 The Avenue, Starbeck, Harrogate, North Yorkshire HG1 4QD.
Lyle, Glenmayne, Galashiels TD1 3NR.
Period Petrol Pump Co., The, Grove Farm, Mill Green, Burston, Diss, Norfolk.
Phillips, 65 George Street, Edinburgh EH2 2JL.
Phillips, Blenstock House, 7 Blenheim Street, New Bond Street, London W1Y 0AS.
Sheffield Railwayana Auctions, 43 Little Norton Lane, Sheffield S8 8GA.
Paul Sheppard, The Vallets, Forge Crossing, Lyonshall, Kington, Herefordshire.
Skinner Inc., Bolton Gallery, Route 117, Bolton MA, USA.
Sotheby's, 34-35 New Bond Street, London W1A 2AA.
Sotheby's, 1334 York Avenue (at 72nd Street), New York, NY 10021, USA.
Street Jewellery, 16 Eastcliffe Avenue, Newcastle Upon Tyne NE3 4SN.
Ute Twite, Togford, Stogumber, Taunton, Somerset TA4 3TN.
T. Vennet Smith, 11 Nottingham Road, Gotham, Nottingham NG11 0HE.
Sam Weller, Ash House, 28 Bure Way, Aylsham, North Norfolk NR11 6HJ.
Cyril Wickham, 26 St. Clares Walk, Brigg, South Humberside DN20 8JS.
Yesterday's Paper, Ivybank House, 122 Upgate, Louth, Lincolnshire LN11 9HG.

Contents

"So near and yet So far."

Sign of the Times

It is the Industrial Revolution which really must bear responsibility for the creation of advertising antiques by bringing about all the changes necessary for the formation of a consumer society. Hitherto, communities had been largely self sufficient, producing what they needed from their own resources and buying the extras from pedlars and the like. If you needed a table, you went to the carpenter; if you needed beer you went to the inn and asked simply for a jug of ale etc. With the Industrial Revolution, however, came an enormous increase in manufacturing capability, with the attendant need to market these wares more widely. Fortunately the coming of the railways and improved travel facilities in general ensured that this was possible.

Thus the manufacturer became separated from the retailer, and shopkeepers and customers alike had to be persuaded to buy branded goods. The fact that literacy was on the increase was a further coincidental factor which helped them to do this. The tradesman's figural hanging symbols designed to guide the illiterate began to disappear in the late 18th century, and a law was in fact passed in 1792, which restricted their size in order to minimize accidents and creaking! Their place was taken by lettered boards and signs which offered greater scope for information about brand names and the range of goods available.

It is interesting that we seem to be regressing from this now, as the coded symbol of an instantly recognisable logo becomes increasingly prevalent. This of course is because we are so constantly bombarded with advertising that the mere sight of the logo triggers off an automatic association with the message in our minds.

But before the age of radio and television, advertising was concentrated in the street rather than in the home, and with no seductive voice-over the lettering had to say it all, while the sign had to be eye-catching too. Manufacturers plagiarised fine art quite shamelessly for their advertising imagery – Landseer's Monarch of the Glen for Dewar's Whisky, or Millais' Bubbles' for Pear's Soap, for example.

" BUBBLES."
By Sir JOHN MILLAIS, Bt., P.R.A.
After the Original in the possession of Messrs. PEARS

Others employed a host of anonymous graphic designers and artists to convey their chosen imagery. New technological advances helped as well. Porcelain enamelling on to iron had, for example, been developed in the early 1800s in Europe, but it was not until 1859 that Benjamin Baugh set up a factory for this process in Britain. Originally they produced panels for church altars and decorative panels, but in 1889 he opened the Patent Enamel Company Ltd for the exclusive production of enamel signs. In the years between then and the Second World War millions of such signs were produced both for the home market and abroad, and other companies sprang up following **Baugh**'s lead. Enamel signs are now one of the principal jewels in the crown of advertising antiques and command such prices that it is advisable

Worthington's In Bottle *china jardinière made by Royal Doulton, 20cm. high.*
(Cyril Wickham) £450

to remove any which remain unguarded in their original position for fear of theft.

There are advertising antiques to suit all pockets and all sizes of available display space. Many were designed for point of sale display, in the form of show cards, models etc. which would stand in a shop and act as a constant reminder to the retailer and his customers. In pubs, brewers and distillers would provide free jugs, coasters and trays for the same purpose.

For all that, there is a certain innocence about advertising antiques, which is probably why they appeal to so many people jaded by today's rampant commercialism. For one thing, many are not just tatty geegaws but are surprisingly well made and have a lasting and intrinsic artistic value of their own. Also, they are neither pushy nor intrusive, nor do they play insidious psychological games with us, as does so much contemporary advertising. It is scarcely to be wondered at then, that advertising antiques have a constantly growing band of devotees, for whom this book should prove an irresistible and invaluable asset.

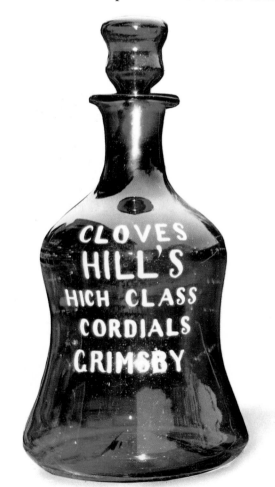

Cloves Hill's High Class Cordials Grimsby, *green glass decanter, 32cm. high.*
(Cyril Wickham) £350

Advertising China Figures

China advertising figures were made by a host of leading ceramic manufacturers. Some carry the message explicitly, while others rely on the familiarity of the image, e.g. the Guinness toucans. Others were specially commissioned in limited editions by the manufacturer.

Liqueur flask depicting **Falstaff** made by Royal Doulton for W. Walklate Ltd.   (Lyle)   £45

Dr Scholl's Zino Pads, counter display china figure made by Doulton, (Dave Lewis)   £75

Bisquit's Brandy figure, water jug, 27cm. high. (Cyril Wickham)   £425

A set of **'Flying Toucans'**, produced for **Guinness** by Carltonware of Stoke-on-Trent, 1930's.   (Dave Lewis)   £200

Charrington's Toby by Royal Doulton, 23cm. high. (Cyril Wickham)   £475

Cliff Cornell, 'Brown suit' jug issued by Doulton in 1956. £350

Dr Scholl's Zino Pads, made by Doulton, 8in. high. (Dave Lewis) £75

Army Club cigarettes display figure made by Doulton. £100

Advertising China Figures

Cognac Martell Brandy
advertising jug by Sanderson,
Hanley, Staffordshire, 6¹/₂in.
high.   (Lyle)   £75

**Scotsman and Irishman
whisky flasks** designed by
Royal Doulton for Asprey & Co.,
New Bond Street, London.
(Lyle)   £3,500

**Cliff Cornell 'Blue suit' Toby
jug** made by Royal Doulton,
1956, 9¹/₄in. high.
(Lyle)   £350

The McCallum, a large
Kingsware character jug made
by Royal Doulton for D & J
McCallum Whisky Distillers,
circa 1930.   (Lyle)   £1,450

Burke's Green Label Whiskey by
Fieldings, Stoke on Trent, 29cm.
high.   (Cyril Wickham)   £625

Yardley's Lavender, ceramic
figure by Dresden, early 20th
century.   (Cyril Wickham) £350

Advertising China Figures

Set of advertising jugs made by Royal Doulton, depicting
Dickens characters, for **Jim Beam Whiskey**, 1984. (Lyle)   £200

Whisky flask in the form of a
crow made for National
Distillers of Kentucky, circa
1954.   (Lyle)   £150

**Greenlees Claymore, The
Favourite Scotch Everywhere,**
display figure, 31cm. high.
(Cyril Wickham)   £550

William Grant advertising jug
specially commissioned by Wm.
Grant & Sons Ltd in a limited
edition of 500, 1986.   £400

Newsvendor designed by W.
Harper in a limited edition of
2,500 for the Newspaper
Society, 1986, 7in. high.   £220

Advertising Mugs

Are advertising mugs one of the subtler forms of selling, designed to form a subconscious association between the product they advertise and the 'good' feelings engendered by a welcome break and a refreshing cup of tea or coffee? They are certainly more popular today than ever, to the extent that people can even be persuaded to buy them!

Smarties.
(Street Jewellery)   £3

Cadburys Chocolate, 1984.
(Street Jewellery)   £10

Insist on Oxo, circa 1880.
(Street Jewellery)   £50

Silver Spoon mug made by Kilnkraft, 1991.
(Street Jewellery)   £2

Nescafe by Kilnkraft, 1991.
(Street Jewellery)   £2

Oxo mug, made in Stoke on Trent, 1980.
(Street Jewellery)   £2

Nescafe 50th Anniversary 1939–1989.
(Street Jewellery)   £2

Kelloggs Raisin Splitz.
(Street Jewellery)   £5

Horlicks advertising mug made by Arklow, circa 1920.
(Street Jewellery)   £15

50th Anniversary **Kit Kat** 1937–1987.
(Street Jewellery)   £5

Bovril, circa 1910.
(Street Jewellery)   £35

Advertising Novelties

These tended to be die cut cards which would be given away at point of sale. Children and animals were by far the favoured subjects and could be used to advertise anything from metal polish to beef extract.

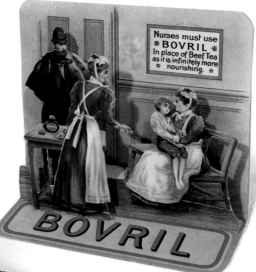

Late 19th century, '**Bovril**' pop-up counter display sign. (Yesterday's Paper)   £25

Pear's Soap, 'You Dirty Boy', 7in. x 5in. (Ute Twite)   £10

Chocolat Suchard Neuchâtel, 4¼in. x 4½in. (Ute Twite)   £5

Cook's Dorina Bath Soap, folding printed card, 5in. high. (Dave Lewis)   £15

Hudsons Extract of Soap, Arrest All Dirt, printed card, 6in. high. (Dave Lewis)   £10

Raphael Tuck & Son's Fire Screens advertising scrap. (Dave Lewis)   £10

13

Advertising Novelties

'Globe Metal Polish, Gives The Shine That Lasts', printed card, 5¹/₂in. high. (Dave Lewis) £10

'Neave's, The Food for Infants', printed card counter display sign, 4¹/₂in. high. (Dave Lewis) £10

Globe Metal Polish, Made in England, 5¹/₂in. high. (Dave Lewis) £10

Ask for the Globe Polish, and see that you get it! (Yesterday's Paper) £12

Dr Lovelace's Soap, Unequalled for every Household Purpose. (Dave Lewis) £8

Ride a Raleigh, The All Steel Bicycle, printed card, 6in. high. (Dave Lewis) £10

Echtes Fleisch – Extract, 5in x 2¹/₂in. (Ute Twite) £5

Chocolat Suchard Neuchâtel, 4¹/₂in. x 5in. (Ute Twite) £10

Borwick's Baking Powder. (Dave Lewis) £10

Advertising Novelties

Chocolat Suchard Neuchâtel,
3³/₄in. x 4³/₄in. (Ute Twite) £8

An ingenious printed card, folding sign for **Sunlight Soap by Lever Bros. Ltd., Soap Makers to the Queen**, 3in. high. (Dave Lewis) £20

Chocolat Suchard Neuchâtel,
4¹/₂in. x 4¹/₂in. (Ute Twite) £8

Joseph Suters Volks Magazin,
4in x 2¹/₂in. (Ute Twite) £5

Suchard, 4³/₄in. x 4¹/₂in. (Ute Twite) £10

Van Houten's Pure Soluble Cocoa. (Dave Lewis) £7

The Globe Metal Polish Extract. (Yesterday's Paper) £12

Van Houten's Pure Soluble Cocoa. (Dave Lewis) £10

'Globe Polish, Paste & Liquid' printed die cut novelty give away, 6in. high. (Dave Lewis) £10

Advertising Novelties

Cadbury's Cocoa Essence,
4in. x 6¹/₂in. (Ute Twite) £10

**Dr Lovelace's Soap, It makes the skin
healthy.** (Dave Lewis) £8

Advertising novelty depicting a face
with nose spectacles. (Dave Lewis) £6

Songs of the Empire for Little Folks, a give-away by
Colman's mustard, circa 1910. (Yesterday's Paper) £8

Advertising Postcards

When the Post Office offered to deliver printed cards for half the cost of a letter in 1869, advertisers were quick to realise the potential of these. However it was not until 1902 that permission was granted for the address and the message to be written on the same side, leaving the other for a picture.

Harrods advertising postcard by Chris Jones, 1986. £2

"TIT-BITS" INSURES YOUR LIFE FOR £1,000.

Tit-bits Insures Your Life for £1,000. £6

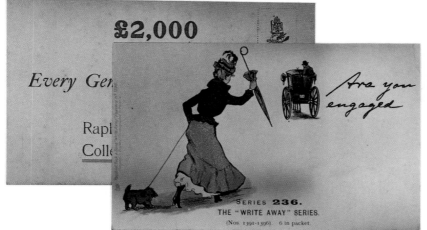

£2,000

Every Ger...

Rapl...
Colle...

SERIES 236.
THE "WRITE AWAY" SERIES.
(Nos. 1391-1396.) 6 in packet.

Are you engaged

Raphael Tuck advertising card. £50

" I hear they want more

BOVRIL

'I hear they want more Bovril'. £12

A NICE PRESENT BRAND ROTHSCHILDS REGALIA

COLORADO

*If the Ladies NICOTINE—you'd see
In all their frills and flounces:
Draw the slide—and a charming pair
Before your vision bounces.*

Rothschild's mechanical cigarette advertising card. £60

THE LAST WORD IN COCOAS

"BOURNVILLE"

Reduced Fac-simile Latest poster universally displayed by **CADBURYS**

The last word in Cocoas, Bournville. £5

POST FROM Barnstaple

Post from Barnstaple with fold out photographs. £15

Advertising Postcards

Van Houtens Cocoa, The Little Pets' Breakfast, chromolithograph card. £8

Fry's Chocolate Special issued by The House of Fry, Somerdale in Somerset. £10

Portola Festival, San Francisco, 1909. £8

Plaxtons, 17/18 Seater Consort Body. £7

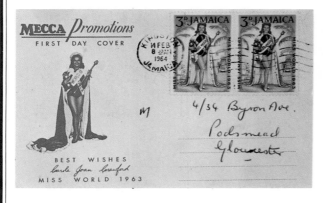

Mecca Promotions, Miss Jamaica, 1963. £5

BOAC Cunard 3D postcard. £8

Shell Motor Spirit, Old King Cole. £25

You Don't Know Beans until you come to Boston. £5

(Paul Sheppard)

Advertising Postcards

Ridgways Tea, mechanical card, 1901. £35

Hixopad Rubber Heels, The Best. £6

The Philips Lamp. £20

Pear's Soap, 'Bubbles'. £3

Guinness advertising card. £2

Jungle Oats featuring **Gary Player.** £10

Cooks Lightning Soap postcard. £25

Telephone advertising card. £20

Tucks, Defenders of the Empire. £12

(Paul Sheppard)

Advertising Signs

There have been advertising signs of all kinds for hundreds of years. The most valuable of all, however, are the wooden figures designed to stand particularly outside tobacco shops, not only the classic 'cigar store Indian' but also kilted Highlanders which will now fetch thousands of pounds.

A painted wood **'Dapper Dan'** trade sign, Philadelphia, circa 1880, 77¼in. high. (Sotheby's) £183,333

A carved and painted **cigar store Indian**, American, late 19th century, 72½in. high. (Christie's) £7,650

19th century tobacconist's, carved wood and polychrome sign of a **soldier in Highland dress**, 69in. high. (Christie's) £9,350

Snuffing Highlander from Bacon's the Tobacconist, Cambridge, 84in. high. (Christie's) £8,800

Carved and painted figure of an **Indian squaw**, American, circa 1870, 45½in. high. (Skinner Inc) £14,850

Advertising Vehicles

The manufacturing boom of the 19th and early 20th centuries was facilitated by the improvements in transport, first with the railways and then on the roads. It was a logical step therefore that the vehicles which carried the goods should also advertise them.

Dinky John Menzies Bedford van, 1974. (Jim Binns) £25

Chivers Jellies, Trojan van, 1953. (Jim Binns) £30

Royal Mail Bedford van, 1972. (Jim Binns) £75

Dunlop, Trojan van, 1953. (Jim Binns) £25

Oxo Beef at its Best, pre war 28d delivery van. (Christie's) £1,540

H.J. Heinz Co., by Matchbox, 1930 Ford A. (Street Jewellery) £15

Cerebos Table Salt by Matchbox, 1930 Ford A. (Street Jewellery) £25

PG Tags – just the ticket by Lledo. (Street Jewellery) £7

Ovaltine, Bedford van, 1955. (Jim Binns) £30

Advertising Vehicles

Chivers Breakfast Marmalade by Lledo. £6

McVities Digestive, Model A Ford, 1979. £10

Shredded Wheat by Lledo. £6

Kellogg's Corn Flakes by Corgi. £6

Asda Premium British Sausages by Lledo. £6

Vosene by Lledo. £6

Tetley's Tea by Lledo. £10

Warburtons by Lledo. £6

Kellogg's Corn Flakes by Matchbox. £6

Oxydol 'For Whiter Whites' by Lledo. £6

Ringtons Tea by Lledo. £10
(Street Jewellery)

Advertising Vehicles

W.H. Smith & Son Ltd by
Matchbox.   £6
Shell Petroleum Products by
Corgi.   £6
Rowntree's Table Jelly by
Matchbox.   £6
Fina Morris Truck by Corgi.£10
Be-Ro Self-raising Flour by
Lledo.   £6
Macleans by Lledo.   £6
Stabilo Boss, A.E.C. Van by
Corgi.   £6
Cadbury's Drinking Chocolate
by Lledo.   £6
Kellogg's Rice Krispies by
Matchbox.   £6
Osram Lamps, Bedford Bus by
Corgi.   £6
Wells Jaffa Orange Drinks by
Lledo.   £6
(Street Jewellery)

Ashtrays

Watson's No. 10 Scotch ashtray matchholder.
(Lyle) £100

1950's Guinness ashtray with Dickens decoration, 3¹/₂in. diameter.
(Muir Hewitt) £35

Kings Liqueur, Finest Scotch Whisky.
(Dave Lewis) £35

1938 Glasgow Exhibition ashtray in chrome with butterfly wing decoration.
(Muir Hewitt) £25

Metal ashtray mounted with an Alfa Romeo 158 made by Alfa to celebrate their victory in the world championships, 1950.
(Finarte) £670

King George IV Old Scotch Whisky ashtray.
(Lyle) £75

John Haig's Whisky ashtray.
(Cyril Wickham) £50

Schweppes soda water ashtray.
(Cyril Wickham) £50

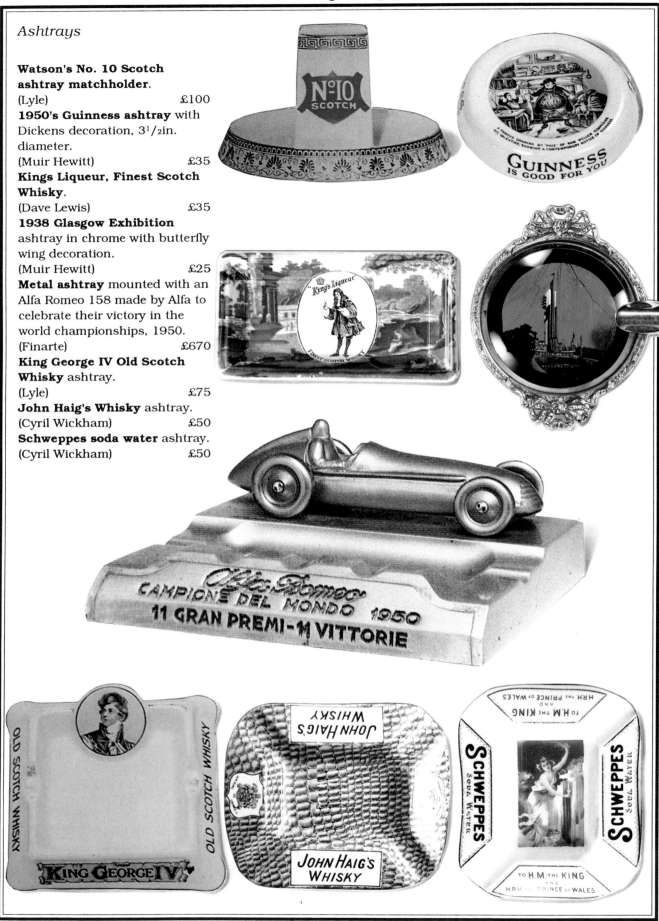

Bill Heads

Whether it just made the bills easier to 'swallow', if you had an elaborate billhead at the top of your account, or whether the invoicee was meant to be so overwhelmed by the might and majesty of the company that he coughed up at once, is open to doubt.

Horner, Son & Co., manufacturing Clothiers, 1917.
(Yesterday's Paper) £3
Jebb Brothers Ltd., Newcastle-on-Tyne, 1922.
(Yesterday's Paper) £3
W. D. & H. O. Wills & Sons, Tobacco & Snuff manufacturers, 1874.
(Yesterday's Paper) £3
F. Fleck, Sanitary Plumber,
1918. (Yesterday's Paper) £3
Chas Ley, Cooper in General, 1837.
(Yesterday's Paper) £5

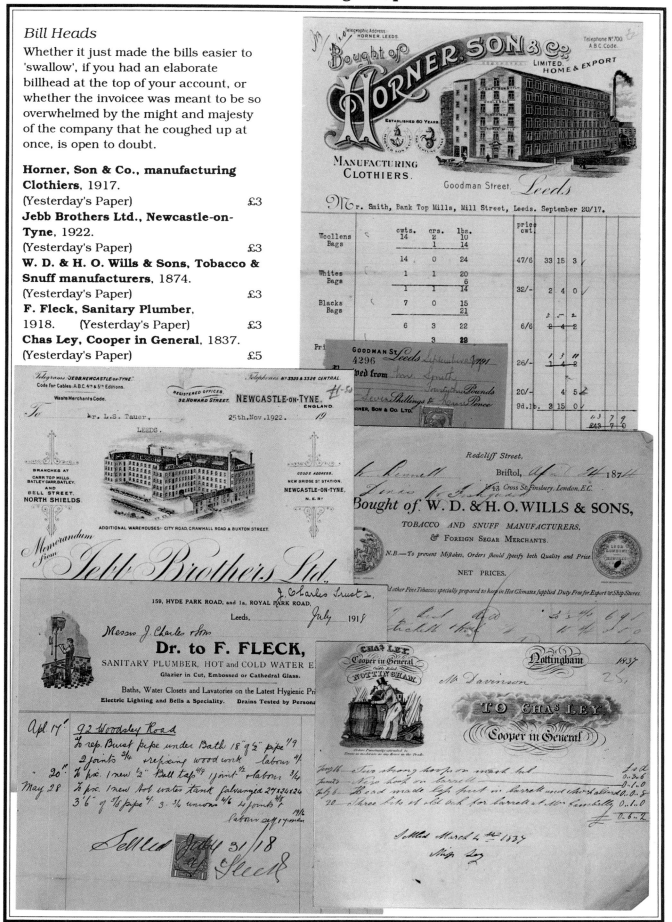

Bill Heads

A.I. Greenwood, Cycle and Motor Factor and Manufacturer, 1921.
£2

J. Hopkinson & Co., Huddersfield, Contactors to H.M. Government and The Admiralty, 1894. £5

R. Barr, Motor Char-A-Banc proprietor, 1926. £3

G.S. Jackson, Bill Poster & Town Crier, 1884. £3

Mars Confections Ltd, Slough Bucks, 1941. £3

(Yesterday's Paper)

Bill Heads

**Robert Stott, Cotton Spinner,
Alexandra Mills, Oldham**, 1892. £3
Richard Groves & Sons, 1851. £5
**Dan Dawson Bros., Huddersfield,
1893.** £4
**The Midland Railway Carriage &
Wagon Company Ltd.,
Birmingham, 1897** £5
**John Bragg & Son, Motor Haulage
& Carting Contractors, 1919.** £3
(Dave Lewis)

Blotters

Before the age of the ballpoint pen, blotters were a standard feature of every office and home. And because you spent time staring at them as you tried to compose your letter, wrestle with your accounts, or whatever, they were a superb advertising medium.

Graftons Chiffonelle for dainty Lingerie, Blouses, Day Wraps and Dresses, printed blotter.　(Lyle)　£15

'Ridgways Ltd., Tea & Coffee Importers & Merchants', printed blotter, circa 1905.
(Dave Lewis)　£15

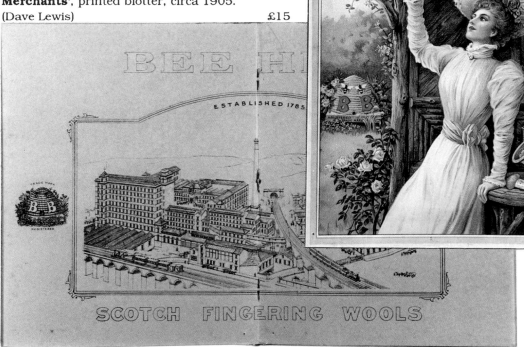

Beehive Wheeling, Fingering & Knitting Wools, printed blotter, circa 1905.
(Dave Lewis)　£20

Bookmarks

Printed paper bookmarks date from the mid 19th century. They have attracted a varied range of advertisers, among whom investment and insurance companies predominate, probably because they were targeting a more affluent book buying public.

It is well worth taking the time to sort through the stocks of second hand books at jumble sales and other fund raising events for treasures can often be found nestling between the pages.

Keens D.S.F. Mustard, made of celluloid. £10
Boots Book Lovers Library, celluloid, 1920. £10
Halifax Building Society 1930's. £2
St Ivel Cheese, Crusader figure. £5
P & P Campbell, The Perth Dye Works, circa 1900. £3
Children Love Book Tokens, 1960's. £1
B.B. (Better Books) O.U.P., 1960's. £1
Dickens Bookmark from the Sunday Companion, 1924. £3
Feltoe's Lime Juice Cordial, 1910. £4
Lloyds Weekly News, The Best Family Paper, circa 1910. £8
Anic Cigarettes, circa 1950. £2
Hall's Distemper, 70 Tints to select from, circa 1930. £3
British Dominions Fire Office, circa 1930. £2
School Health Services, 1950. £2
Northern of London & Aberdeen. £3
Wire Haired Fox Terrier. £2
Pears Soap watch fob and seal, 1910. £5
'Good King Wenceslas', Studio Mag Insert, 1930. £3
(Yesterday's Paper)

Bottles

Bottle collecting is a complex field, often categorised according to original contents, or colour, origin or shape. In the days of mass illiteracy, poison and medicine bottles would have highly characteristic shapes and virulent colours to alert the unwary. More information however was obviously desirable and this was first done by embossing or impressed marks on the glass. By the 1830s, however, most bottles bore some sort of paper label.

Furmoto Pine Disinfectant screw top bottle. (Sam Weller) £2

C.F. Goole Pontypridd green Codds bottle, Beaves patent. £150

E.G. Booz's figural whisky bottle 7³/₄in. high. (Skinner Inc.) £575

Harrison's Columbia Ink gallon size bottle, (Skinner Inc) £6,285

Suffolk Bitters figural pig bottle with flattened collared lip, 10in. long, 1875. (Skinner Inc) £235

Wasp Waist poison bottle patented 1894. £450

Propert's Standard Blacking. (Dave Lewis) £10

'Pure Milk' screw top jar, Adlam patent. (Lyle) £500

1960's Tour de France drinks bottle, 6in. high. (Sam Weller) £5

French wire encased soda syphon, 18in. high. £95

Parker Bros. Drighlington, syphon. £20

Aquaperia 10¹/₂in. high. (Dave Lewis) £10

Crying Baby figural bottle, 6in. high, 1875. (Skinner) £60

Bottles

South Hants Mineral Water Co amber bottle. (Cyril Wickham) £150

Izal disinfectant triangular green glass bottle with screw top. £2

O'Reillys Patent Binocular Poison bottle, 1905. (Lyle) £800

Cream Emulsion of Cod Liver Oil bottle. (Dave Lewis) £5

Skull figural poison bottle 4$^1/_8$in. high. (Skinner) £800

Moses figural **Poland Springs** mineral water bottle, 10$^7/_8$in. high. (Skinner) £95

Holt & Co. amber bottle, Edwards patent. (Cyril Wickham) £200

Pineapple figural bitters bottle, 1860. (Skinner) £575

Six sided poison bottle embossed with **Savory's Patent**, circa 1860. (Lyle) £500

Green glass chemist's bottle **'Liq Arsenic'**, 7in. high. £10

Kingsware Whisky bottle made for Bulloch Wade, circa 1919. (Lyle) £120

Optrex Eye Lotion bottle complete with eyebath. £5

Blue Soyer bottle with metal stand. £325

Wire mesh encased soda syphon, 12in. high. £35

Calendars

Calendars

Calendars

Lamb's Rum calendar, 1981.
(Yesterday's Paper)   £6

The Lord of the Rings calendar, 1977.
(Yesterday's Paper)   £10

Pentax calendar by Sam Haskins, 1981.
(Yesterday's Paper)   £12

1950's calendar by Dickens for **'Hunt for the Best'**. (Yesterday's Paper)   £12

Card Signs

Card signs served much the same purpose as the poster, though they were more robust and often came already framed, for hanging permanently on the wall of a shop or pub. They were particularly prominent in the last two decades of the last century.

'Ye sampler of Birds Custard', card sign.
(Dave Lewis)   £25

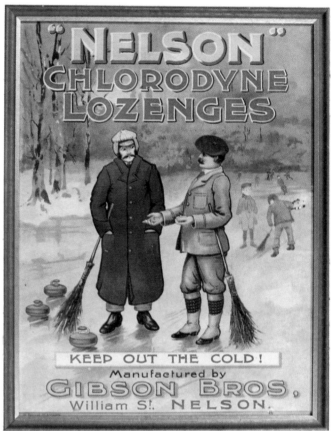

Printed card sign for **Nelson Chlorodyne Lozenges**, manufactured by Gibson Bros., William St., Nelson.
(Dave Lewis)   £120

The Swansea Brewery Co., framed advertisement, 34in. x 28in.
(Cyril Wickham)   £300

'Abram Lyle & Sons Golden Syrup, printed card shop display stack of tins, 13in. high. (Dave Lewis)   £20

Card Signs

Buckling, Treasure of the Sea, showcard, 12in. high. (Sam Weller) £5

Mansion Polish, display card, circa 1930. (Lyle) £25

Nobel Industries Ltd display board, 79cm. x 64cm. (Phillips) £1,750

The Sportsman Outfit framed advertisement, 19in. x 24in. (Cyril Wickham) £225

Card Signs

**Westlake's Ales &
Stout** framed
advertisement,
37in. x 27in.
(Cyril Wickham)
£500

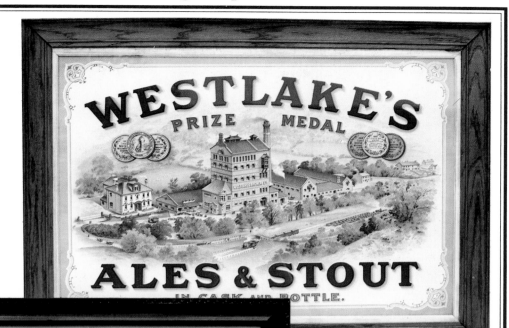

**Sutton's Extra
Stout**, Britannia
Brewery, Brigg,
framed
advertisement,
23in. x 30in.
(Cyril Wickham)
£450

**Peek Frean
Biscuits** framed
advertisement.
(Sheffield
Railwayana
Auctions) £250

Card Signs

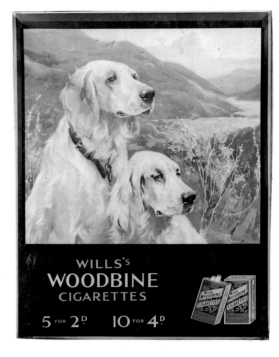

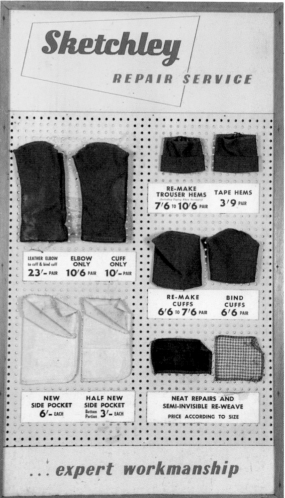

Card Signs

Felinfoel Celebrated Pale Ale, framed card
sign, 14in. x 18in.
(Cyril Wickham) £125
Wills Woodbine Cigarettes, printed card
sign.
(Cyril Wickham) £100
**Gallaher Ltd., Golden Spangled
Cigarettes**, framed advertisement, 18in. x
22in.
(Cyril Wickham) £225
Sketchley Repair Service sample board,
25in. high, 1960's.
(Sam Weller) £18
Right
Printed card sign for **Fry's Pure
Concentrated Coco**a,
**'Home through the snow our Pierrot hies,
Warmed with a cheering cup of Fry's'**,
in original frame, circa 1900.
(Dave Lewis) £250
**Wm. Hancock & Co. Ltd., 'I wonder if
they'd miss a bottle'**, card sign, 31in. x
21in.
(Cyril Wickham) £200
Printed card for **The Celebrated Yorkshire
Relish, The Most Delicious Sauce in the
World**, 15in. x 20in.
(Dave Lewis) £100

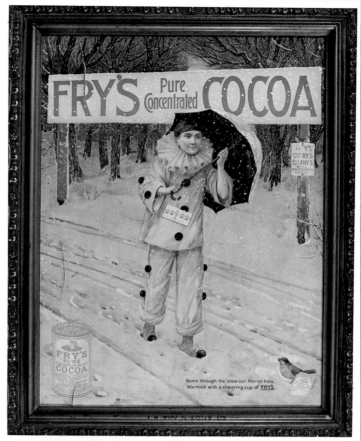

Card Signs

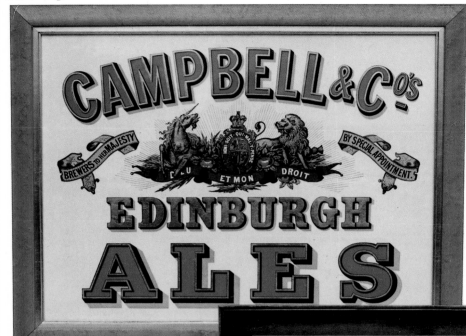

Campbell & Co's., Edinburgh Ales, framed poster, 20in. x 16in. (Cyril Wickham) £75

Brain's Red Dragon, The Beer that sets the Standard, framed poster, 21in. x 26in.. (Cyril Wickham) £175

Palethorpes Royal Cambridge Sausages, 22in. x 17in. (Cyril Wickham) £275

Card Signs

Franklyn's Shagg 'A cool customer and a cool smoke', framed advertisement, 22in. x 19in.   (Cyril Wickham)   £325

Fry's Cocoa 'So near and yet so far' framed advertisement, 18in. x 23in. (Cyril Wickham)   £450

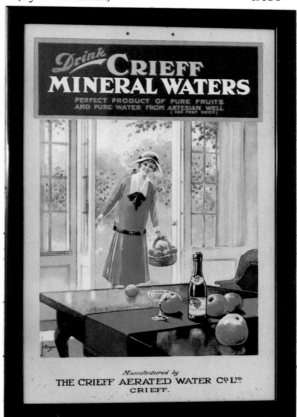

W.D. & H.O. Wills Ltd., Cinderella cigarettes, framed advertisement, 18in. x 22in. (Cyril Wickham)   £225

Crieff Mineral Waters, display sign, 12in. x 17in. (Cyril Wickham)   £125

Chocolate Boxes

Kunzle 'Presentation Dessert Chocolates', 8in. x 4in., 1930's. £4

Kunzle 'Check' assorted chocolates, 8in. x 4in., circa 1930's. £4

Kunzle 'Milk & Plain' assorted chocolates, 8in. x 4in., 1930's. £4

Fuller's Chocolates 'Mount Everest' Assortment, circa 1953, 6in. x 3in. £9

Cadbury's Dairy Milk Chocolate Neapolitans, 8in. x 4in. £6

Rowntree's Chocolates, 6in. x 2in. £6

Kunzle 'Cracknut' assorted chocolates, 8in. x 4in., 1930's. £8

Genuine Spirit Liqueur Chocolates, printed card box by Betty's Ltd., Harrogate, 9in. long. £25

Kunzle 'City' assorted chocolates, 5in. high, circa 1930's. £8
(Sam Weller)

Clocks

What better place to locate an advertisement than on the thing which everyone watches – the clock! Value depends a good deal on the product being advertised – a Coca Cola clock for example is always one to look out for.

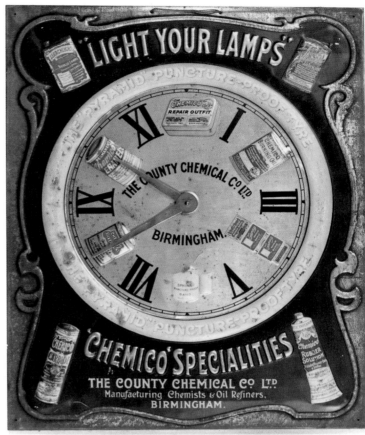

EverReady Safety Razor advertising clock with American 8 day movement.
(Auction Team Köln)   £400

Chemico Specialities embossed tin clock, made for The County Chemical Co. Ltd., Burmingham.
(Dave Lewis)   £130

Chemico Specialities 'Light Your Lamps' embossed clock produced for The County Chemical Co. Ltd., Birmingham. (Dave Lewis) £130

Advertising clock for Palethorpes Sausages, 1940's, 12in. square.
(Dave Lewis)   £75

Coasters

These are not the down-market bits of cardboard one finds under one's glass nowadays in most pubs, but elaborately decorated ceramic coasters, some with silver mounts, which complemented the florid Gothic interiors of some Victorian City pubs. Their purpose, however, was the same, with the decoration advertising the brew which the manufacturers hoped the customer would be quaffing. Again, the nature of their function has meant that surviving examples in good condition are very rare. Most were produced by the prestigious Copeland company, and some are marked Cauldon and even Minton. Their rarity means that a slight degree of damage is generally acceptable to collectors.

Wm. Younger & Co. India Pale Ale, 6in. diameter.   £200
Benskins Watford Brewery coaster, 5¹/₂in. diameter.   £250
Allsopp's 'two labels' coaster, 6in. diameter.   £250
Robert Porter & Co., Bulldog coaster, 6in. diameter.   £200
Guild & Wyllie's Pale Ale coaster, 5¹/₂in. diameter.   £200
Allsopp's Pale Ale wheatsheaf coaster, 6in. diameter.   £200
Allsopp & Sons three labels coaster, 6in. diameter.   £275
Dewar's Perth Whisky coaster, 6in. diameter.   £250
(Cyril Wickham)

Counter Display Boxes

These attractive boxes could be described as forming part of the earliest self service system. Designed for prominent display at point of sale, they at once advertised the product and contained it, so that the customer could simply make his selection and lift it out. The only disadvantage was that space on a counter would be limited, and so only a few of these boxes could be used at once.

Pal Hollow Ground Blades, counter display pack complete with contents. (Sam Weller) £8

Palmitine Candles, 9in. long, complete with contents. (Dave Lewis) £15

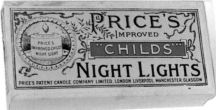

Printed Export box for **Tate & Lyle** cube sugar, 1880's, 18in. wide. (Street Jewellery) £8

Counter display box for **'The Luton Straw Hat Dyes'**, made of card, 11in. wide. (Dave Lewis) £30

Price's Improved Child's Night Lights counter display box, 7in. long. (Dave Lewis) £8

Counter Display Boxes

Counter display box for **Adshead's Metal Paste** complete with contents.
(Dave Lewis)   £25
Edwardian **'Zebra Grate Polish'**, counter display box for 1 gross in sixpenny packets, 14¹/₂in. wide.
(Dave Lewis)   £30
Counter display box for **'Cook's Lotus Toilet Soap'**, 1927, printed card, 8in. long, complete with contents.
(Dave Lewis)   £40
Victorian **'W. Berry's Celebrated Diamond Oil Blacking'**, counter display box, 12in. wide. (Dave Lewis)   £30

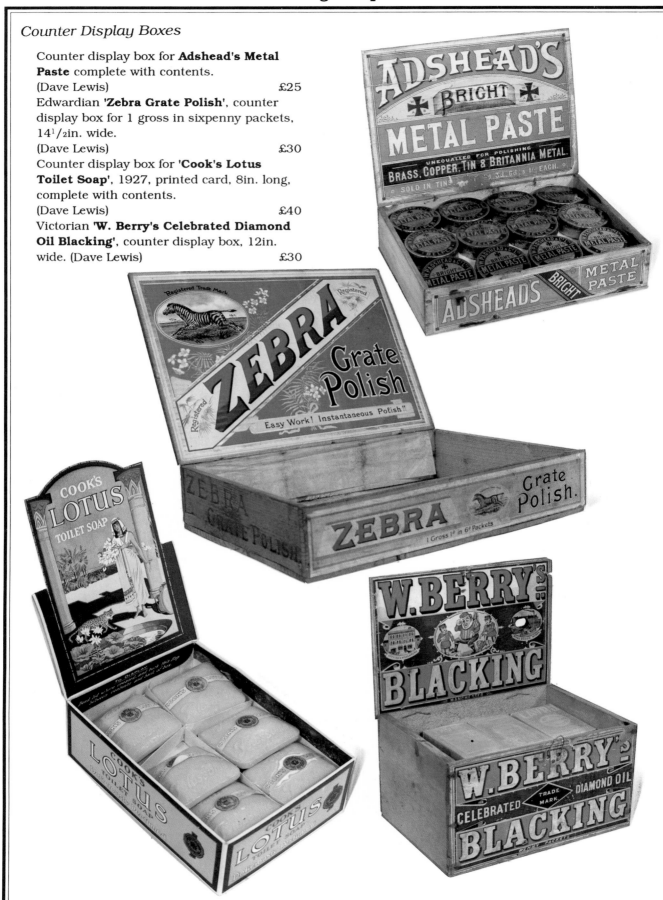

Counter Display Boxes

Counter display box for
**'Broxburn Paraffin Self-Fitting
Candles'**, 7in. long, complete
with contents.
(Dave Lewis)   £15

'Fry's Chocolate Medallion',
printed wooden box, 10in. x
7in., circa 1910.,
(Street Jewellery)   £35

Oxygen Straw Cleaner, printed
cardboard display box, 13in. x
6¹/₂in., complete with contents,
including 80 sachets of cleaner
powder, circa 1905.
(Sam Weller)   £55

'The Electrical Decoration Set', made by the **Japan Federation Lamp
Manufacturer's Association**, 20in. long.
(Dave Lewis)   £35

Dispensers

There is something quite irresistible to the child in us in putting your money in the slot and getting something out the other end. Perhaps that is why so many sweets were sold in dispensers, some of which were really quite stylish.

Columbus Model Ball Chewing Gum dispenser, circa 1932.
(Costa/Bates) £100

Tyne Sava Cigarette Vendor, circa 1935.
(Costa/Bates) £125

Sentimentality candy dispenser.
(Costa/Bates) £75

Player's Cigarettes dispenser for **'Batchelor'** and **'Gold Leaf'**, 26in. high, 1969.
(Sam Weller) £45

Southalls **'Santowel'** wooden dispenser, 27in. high.
(Sam Weller) £18

Display Boxes

In the days before the supermarket, when grocer's shops had real shop windows and goods displayed in them, these usually consisted not of the genuine article, which would perish or 'go off' but of special replica tins, packets and boxes provided specially for display purposes.

Crawford's Royal George Biscuit, cardboard box, 9in. wide, for use as display. (Dave Lewis) £35

Barlova Malt container, 5$\frac{1}{2}$in. high, circa 1945. (Sam Weller) £3

Shop delivery container for **Player's Airman** cigarettes, 1950's. (Sam Weller) £5

Christy's of London hat box. (Lyle) £15

Klem Kompleat Curtain Brackets, 3in. high, 1920's. (Sam Weller) £2

Bryant & May's giant display matchbox complete with matches, 12in. x 7in. (Sam Weller) £15

M.A. Thedford & Co., Liver Medicine. (Sam Weller) £9

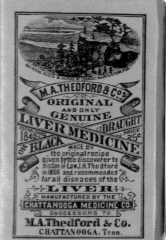

Display Boxes

(Dave Lewis)

Display Boxes

Left

'Lutona Natural Cocoa', printed card shop display box, 10in. high. £15

C.W.S. Pelaw & Silvertown Health Salt, printed card box made by C.W.S. Printing Works, Longsight, Manchester, 9in. long. £35

Eucryl Tooth Powder, 'Makes Teeth Like Pearls', card shop display box, 10$\frac{1}{2}$in. high. £20

'Rowntree's Cocoa', The half-teaspoonful cocoa, cardboard, shop display box, 23in. x 14in. £55

'Plasmon Cocoa, The Mainstay of Life', printed card shop display box, 9in. high. £15

Edwardian **'Holbrook's Worcestershire Sauce'**, printed cardboard box, 9in. wide, to use for shop display. £45

'Rowntree's Cocoa', display box of cardboard construction, 20in. high. £45

'Dee & Ess Cocoa, British Made, Gives Strength to Endure', printed card box, 9in. high. £10

Rowntree's Elect Cocoa, Purity Strength Flavour, cardboard shop display box, 23 x 14in. £55

Right

Shop display box of printed card for **'Luton Straw Hat Dyes'**, by Whitaker & Co., Colour Works, Kendal, 13in. high. £35

'Crawford's Maryland Biscuits', printed cardboard box, 9in. wide, for use as display. £35

'Scotts Porage Oats, The Food of a Mighty Race' printed card box, 9in. high. dummy pack for window display. £15

'Crawford's Golf Biscuits', printed, 9in. wide, cardboard box for window display. £35

Jacob & Co's Chocolate Biscuits, Milk Chocolate Mallow, in printed card box, 1920's, 9in. square. £25

'Crawford's Meadow Creams', printed cardboard box, 9in. wide for use as display. £35

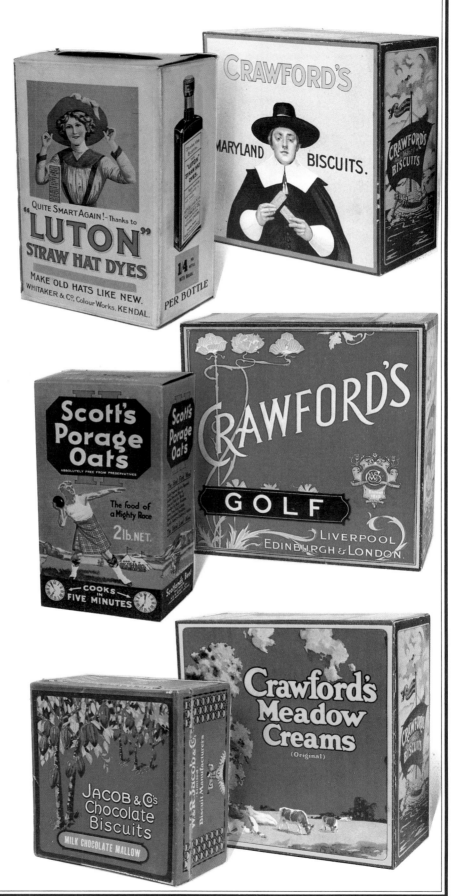

(Dave Lewis)

Display Furniture

'RESTU', Washes White Overnight, advertising chair on turned legs with stretchers, circa 1920. (Street Jewellery)   £100

Fry's Chocolate' cabinet manufactured by **R. Palmer, Jubilee Works, Bristol,** 3ft. tall. (Dave Lewis)   £350

'Watson's Matchless Cleanser is the best Soap', advertising chair on turned legs with stretchers, circa 1910. (Dave Lewis)   £125

Edwardian display cabinet for **Ogden's Ltd Cigarettes** with sideloading drawers, 30in. x 25^1/$_2$in. (Dave Lewis)   £300

Display Packets

Huntley & Palmer's 'Hippodrome' chocolate biscuits, **dummy**, 1930's. (Sam Weller) £10

McVitie & Price's chocolate bar, dummy, 1930's. (Sam Weller) £10

Rowntree's Milk Motoring chocolate bar, dummy. (Sam Weller) £8

Player's Weights Cigarettes display packet, 13$\frac{1}{2}$in. high. (Sam Weller) £10

'Wheat Sheaf Tablet' starch box of printed card, 5in. wide, made by **C.W.S. Products**. (Dave Lewis) £15

McVitie & Price 'Golfer' chocolate bar, dummy, 1930's. (Sam Weller) £10

'Bird's Lemonade, The New Drink with the Real Fruit Flavour', shop display packet, 9in. wide. (Dave Lewis) £35

W.D. & H.O. Wills, Gold Flake Cigarettes, display packet, 12in. high. (Sam Weller) £10

J. Sainsbury's Broadacres Breakfast Food, display packet, 9in. high, 1930's. (Sam Weller) £5

Shop display packet for **President Pink Carbolic Soap**, of printed card construction, 18in. wide. (Dave Lewis) £25

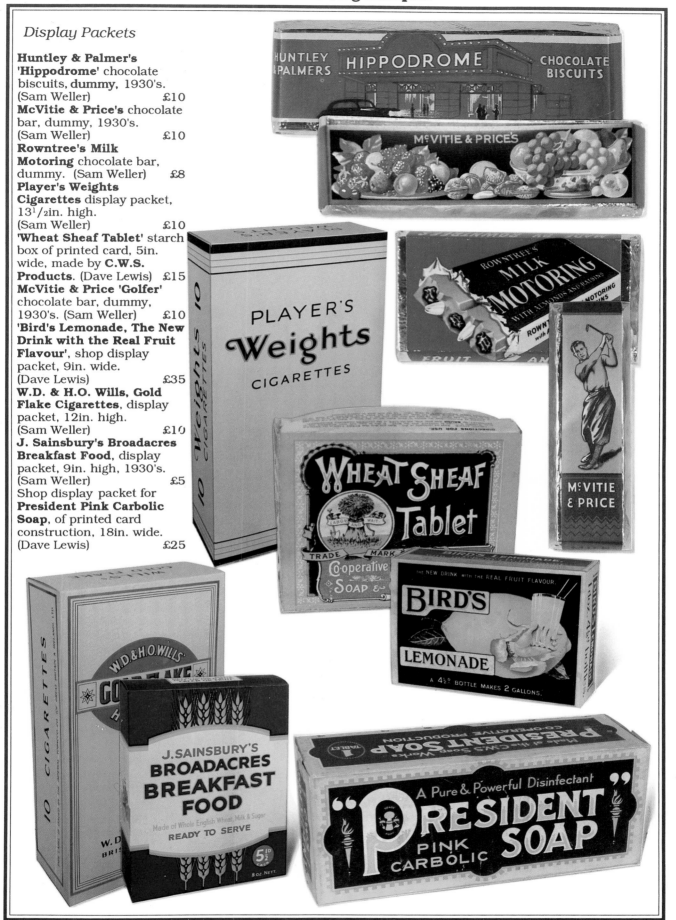

Display Packets

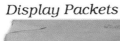

Left

'Stork Margarine', printed card shop display packet, 12in. wide. £30

'Bird's Custard Powder', Edwardian printed card shop display packet, 11in. high. £35

'Van Houten's Cocoa, Best & Goes Farthest', card display packet, 9in. wide. £35

Early 20th century large wooden bottle with paper label advertising **'Service' Brand Coffee**, for shop display, 36in. high. £200

'Bournville Cocoa', card shop display packet, 10in. high. £15

'Meltonian Shoe Cream for good shoes', wooden brush with printed metal hand hold, 4in. long. £10

Right

Huntley & Palmers Ltd Biscuits, display packet, 9in. high. £10

McVitie & Price 'Cricketer' chocolate bar, dummy, 1930's. £9

'Shredded Wheat, Britons Make It – It Makes Britons', printed card display packet, 7¹/₂in. wide. £20

'OXO, for good gravy', printed card shop display packet, 8in. wide. £10

Printed card window display packet for **'Camp Coffee with Chicory'**, 14in. high. £25

1930's, printed card shop display packet for **'Semolina, The Cream of The Wheat'**, 13in. high, for Scottish Wholesale Co-operative Society. £25

Printed card shop display packet for **'Ryvita, crisp nourishing daily bread**, 11in. high. £15

Die-cut shop display sign of printed card construction for **Kolynos Dental Cream**, 21in. high £15

(Dave Lewis)

Display Packets

(Dave Lewis)

Display Tins

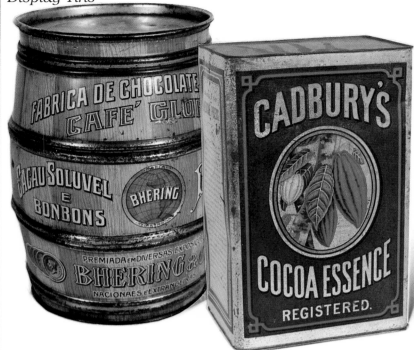

Display tin for **Bhering & Co.,
Cacau Soluvel e Bonbons**, 9in.
high.
(Lyle)   £20

'**Cadburys Cocoa Essence**' shop
display tin, 16in high.
(Dave Lewis)   £35

Lin-Can '**Canned Vegetables
display tin**', 15in high.
(Sam Weller)   £24

Edwardian cardboard shop
display for **Bournville Cocoa**
manufactured by Walter
Fletcher, 'The Improved
Collapsible Show Tin', 16in.
high.
(Dave Lewis)   £85

Cerebos salt tin, large
simulated cardboard shop
display tin manufactured by
Walter Fletcher (Ilford) Ltd.,
19in. high.
(Dave Lewis)   £120

Half-rounded shop display tin
for '**Monk & Glass Custard
Powder**', made of cardboard by
Walter Fletcher (Ilford) Ltd.,
15in high.
(Dave Lewis)   £75

Display Tins

McVitie & Price biscuits, Princess Assorted, Rich Tea and Lincoln Cream.
(Dave Lewis) £10 each

Carnation Evaporated Milk, half-rounded printed card counter display tin, 12½in. high.
(Dave Lewis) £25

Ovaltine, Tonic Food Beverage, half-rounded printed card counter display tin, 14in. high.
(Dave Lewis) £20

Fry's Pure Breakfast Cocoa, large simulated cardboard tin, manufactured by Walter Fletcher (Ilford) Ltd., 19in. high.
(Dave Lewis) £120

Huntley & Palmers Biscuits sample display tin, 1¾in. high.
(Street Jewellery) £25

Bovril Improves the Dishes, display tin, 8in. high, Edwardian.
(Dave Lewis) £25

Victory V, Be as happy as Jolly Jack, printed display tin, 9½in. high.
(Dave Lewis) £15

Display Tins

'Cadburys Cocoa Essence' Edwardian display tin, 8in high. (Dave Lewis) £25

Day & Martin's Wax Boot Polish, 1¹/₂in diameter. (Street Jewellery) £5

Cadbury's Cocoa display tin label, 6¹/₂in. high, Edwardian, lowest cash price. (Dave Lewis) £25

Lin-Can 'Canned Fruits display tin', 15in high. (Sam Weller) £24

Little Liver Pills, tin by Stotherts Ltd., Manufacturing Chemists, Atherton, 4in. square. (Dave Lewis) £35

Jacobs biscuit tin in the form of a gypsy caravan, early 20th century. (Jim Binns) £100

Colman's Mustard display tin with Bulls Head Trade Mark, 8in. wide. (Dave Lewis) £35

Ringtons Tea 'Renowned for Purity, Strength and Flavour', 6in. high, 1920. (Street Jewellery) £20

Enamel Signs

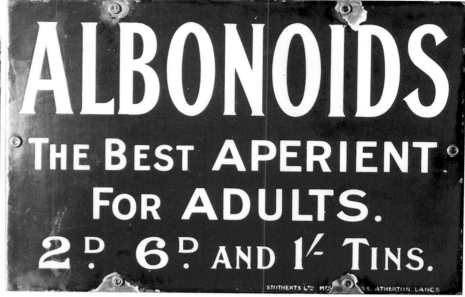

Albonoids The Best Aperient for Adults. (Street Jewellery) £60

The enamelling process of fusing coloured glass to iron had been known about since the early 19th century, but it was not until late in the century that its potential as a medium for advertising signs was recognised and led the Patent Enamel Company to build a factory especially for their production.

The genuine iron based sign has a grey washed back and is more rigid, with clearer colours than the lighter steel versions which began to replace it in the 1920s. The image was applied by stencilling, rubber stamping and the application of lithographic transfers, until this too was superseded by silkscreen printing. Steel shortages during the second World War and the 1950s led to the end of enamel sign production, though nostalgia has recently promoted a small revival.

Matchless Metal Polish, enamel sign, 30in. x 24in. (Street Jewellery) £250

Burma Sauce, The only sauce I dare give father. (Street Jewellery) £100

Van Houten's Cocoa. (Street Jewellery) £250

59

Enamel Signs

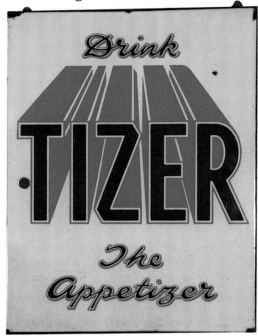

Drink Tizer the Appetizer.

(Street Jewellery)   £45

Hudson's Soap enamel sign, **'A Pail of Water with a very little Hudson's goes a very long way'**, 13¹/₃in. x 9in.   (Dave Lewis)   £80

Old Calabar, Dog Biscuits and Poultry Food.   (Street Jewellery)   £15

Smith's Pinewood Cigarettes.   (Street Jewellery)   £90   **Craven A Virginia Cigarettes.**   £50

Enamel Signs

Lucas Batteries. (Street Jewellery) £50

Player's Navy Cut Cigarettes.
(Street Jewellery) £50

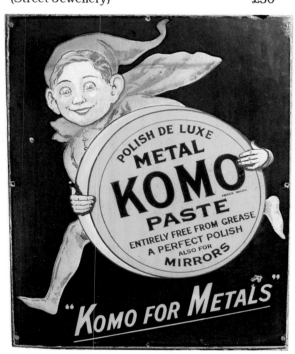

Enamel sign for **Komo Metal Paste**, 24in.
x 30in. (Dave Lewis) £130

Enamel sign for **P. & R. Hay, Dyers and French
Cleaners, Edinburgh**, designed by J.W.
Simpson, 12in. x 24in. (Street Jewellery) £175

Battleaxe Bar. (Street Jewellery) £40

Enamel Signs

Players Navy Cut
cigarettes, 9in. x 6in.
(Street Jewellery) £250

Zebra Grate Polish, 24in. x 24in.,
circa 1900. (Street Jewellery) £250

**Ex-Lax chocolate
laxative.**
(Street Jewellery) £55

St. Bruno, The Standard Dark Flake.
(Street Jewellery) £75

Colman's Mustard with our prime beef, mutton, etc.
(Street Jewellery) £40

Matchless Metal Polish, 30in. x 24in.
(Street Jewellery) £250

Enamel Signs

Eagle & Swan Flours, Rishworth
Ingleby & Lofthouse Ltd., Hull, enamel
sign, 13$\frac{1}{2}$in. x 8in. (Dave Lewis)   £65

Veno's Lightning Cough Cure.
(Street Jewellery)   £85

Get Your Players Please Here.
(Street Jewellery)   £50

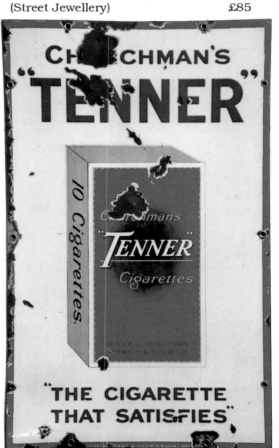

Churchman's Tenner Cigarettes.
(Street Jewellery)   £55

Enamel Signs

Enamel sign for 'Camwal, Like the British Fleet, First in all Waters', 18in. x 48in.   (Dave Lewis)   £90

Thomson's Dye Works Perth.
(Street Jewellery)   £30

Craven "A" Will not affect your throat.   (Street Jewellery)   £40

Ruberoid Roofing, The World's Best, enamel sign made by Willings & Co., 1930's, 36in. x 25in.   (Street Jewellery)   £75

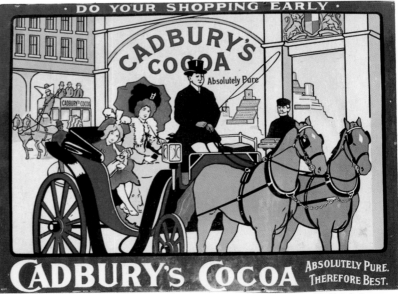

Drink 'Camp', It's the Best, enamel sign.
(Street Jewellery)   £30

Enamel sign for Cadbury's Cocoa manufactured by Falkirk Iron Co., 4ft. x 3ft.   (Dave Lewis)   £400

Enamel Signs

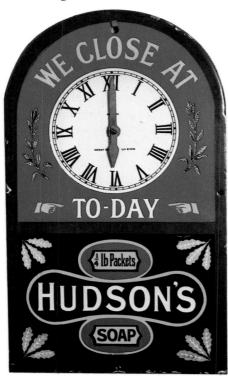

John Sinclair's Rubicon Twist   (Street Jewellery)   £35

Hudson's Soap enamel sign
indicating closing times,
18in. x 10¹/₂in.
(Dave Lewis)   £100

Fremlins Ale enamel sign, 9¹/₂in. high, 12in. long.
(Dave Lewis)   £95

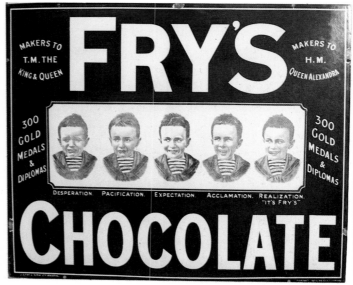

Agent for **Collinson's Tea**.
(Street Jewellery)   £65

Enamel sign for **Fry's Chocolate**, 36in. x 40in.
(Dave Lewis)   £250

Enamel Signs

Birds Custard Powder, 30in. x 20in., circa 1925. (Street Jewellery)   £200

Puck Matches by Bryant & May Ltd.
(Street Jewellery)   £40

Nectar Tea.
(Street Jewellery)   £75

Komo Metal Paste.
(Street Jewellery)   £250

We Sell Sealed Shell.
(Street Jewellery)   £30

Turf Virginia Cigarettes.
(Street Jewellery)   £150

Enamel Signs

Force Wheat Flakes, reproduction
enamel sign.
(Cyril Wickham)   £75

**Walter Willson's Smiling Service
Shops**.
(Street Jewellery)   £75

Daily Telegraph.   (Street Jewellery)   £25

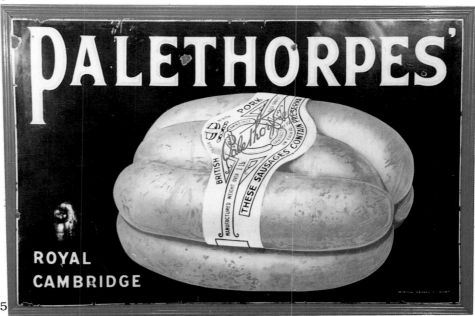

Duckham's Oils.
(Street Jewellery)   £75

Palethorpe's Sausages, Royal Cambridge.   (Street Jewellery)   £125

Enamel Signs

Agent for **Robbialac Paints**, circa 1925, 25in. x 16in.
(Street Jewellery) £100

Sharp's Super-Kreem Toffee
(Street Jewellery) £75

Wincarnis enamel sign, 72in. x 40in.
(Cyril Wickham) £800

Chiver's Carpet Soap, Prized in Royal Households.
(Street Jewellery) £150

B.P. Motor Spirit.
(Street Jewellery) £35

Player's Digger Tobaccos.
(Street Jewellery) £40

Enamel Signs

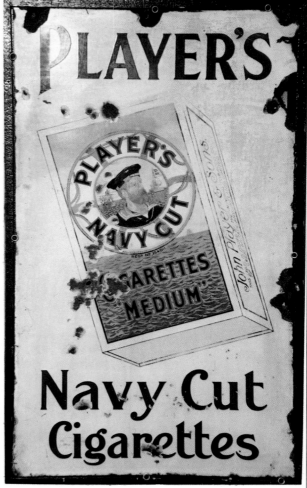

Thorley's Food for Pigs. (Street Jewellery) £100

Stephen's Gum enamel sign, 24in. x 5in. (Street Jewellery) £90

Player's Navy Cut Cigarettes. (Street Jewellery) £60

W.H. Smith enamel sign, circa 1930. (Street Jewellery) £100

Puritan Soap 'Pure as the breeze, 24½ x 37in., circa 1920. (Street Jewellery) £125

Bournville Cocoa, Made by Cadbury. (Street Jewellery) £40

Enamel Signs

Hush!! He's Busy.
(Street Jewellery)   £125

Spratt's 'Builds up a dog!'.
(Street Jewellery)   £35

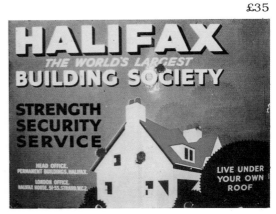

Halifax, The World's Largest Building Society.
(Street Jewellery)   £100

Worthington's India Pale Ale.
(Street Jewellery)   £45

Shell.
(Street Jewellery)   £40

Persil enamel sign, reproduction.
(Cyril Wickham)   £75

Enamel Signs

Ingersoll Watches.
(Street Jewellery)   £80

Printed metal finger
plate for **Yewsabit
Metal Polish**.
(Dave Lewis)   £50

Stop and Fill Up Here With Shell.
(Street Jewellery)   £45

**'There is no tea like
Phillips's**, 40in. x 30in.
(Street Jewellery)   £300

Selo Film enamel sign,
14in. wide.
(Street Jewellery)   £200

Berson's Wack-Em-All Flake Tobacco.
(Street Jewellery)   £45

Enamel Signs

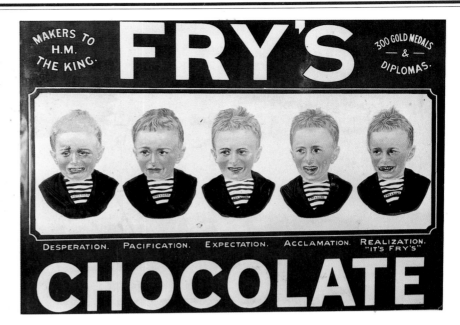

Burnard & Alger's manures, Plymouth.
(Street Jewellery)   £150

Fry's Chocolate 'Five Boys' enamel sign indicating 'Desperation, Pacification, Expectation, Acclamation, Realization It's Fry's'.   (Dave Lewis)   £250

John Bull.   (Street Jewellery)   £20

Singer Sewing Machines, 35in. x 24in.
(Street Jewellery)   £100

Crow Bar dark brown tobacco, 37in. x 24¹/₂in.
(Street Jewellery)   £150

SHELL

Lyons Tea, Degrees Better.
(Street Jewellery)   £80

Shell.   (Street Jewellery)   £30

Enamel Signs

Pickerings Globe Elevator Works.
(Street Jewellery)   £35

Quaker Oats.
(Street Jewellery)   £100

Persil enamel sign made by
Ferro Email, 23in. x 15in.,
circa 1930.
(Street Jewellery)   £80

**Cadbury's Cocoa Essence,
Guaranteed Pure Cocoa,**
enamel sign, 18in. x 11¹/₂in.
(Dave Lewis)   £120

Sun Insurance office.
(Street Jewellery)   £100

Spa thermometer.
(Street Jewellery)   £80   **Drink Tizer The Appetizer.**   (Street Jewellery)   £25

Enamel Signs

Dagenite, the dependable accumulators.
(Street Jewellery) £50

The Nugget Waterproof Black Polish.
(Street Jewellery) £40

Belga, Vander Elst.
(Street Jewellery) £65

The Smoker's Match 'Swan Vestas'.   (Street Jewellery) £60

Vantas Sparkling Drinks.
(Street Jewellery) £45

Smoke Player's Navy Cut.
(Street Jewellery) £85

Enamel Signs

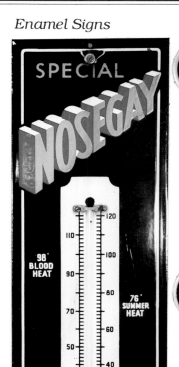

Special Nosegay
Cigarettes.
(Street Jewellery)   £60

Lid Bond Ned, Handelaren in Brandstoffen, 8in. x 12in.
(Street Jewellery)   £45

A.C., Oil Filters, Plugs.
(Street Jewellery)   £50

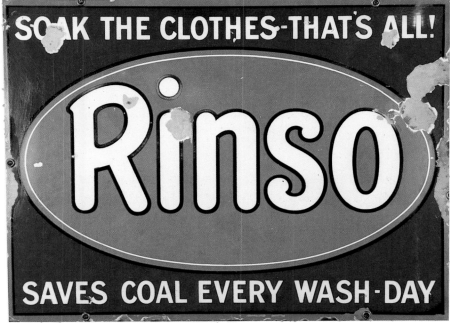

Rinso, Saves Coal Every Wash Day.
(Street Jewellery)
                          £75

Bovril 'Oh Mamma don't
forget to order Bovril', 1896.
(Street Jewellery)   £400

Enamel Signs

Cleveland Petrols.
(Street Jewellery)   £75

Karpol, buy it here.
(Street Jewellery)   £100

Turf Virginia cigarettes
(Sheffield Railway Auctions)   £150

Spratt's Ovals.
(Sheffield Railway Auctions)   £100

Cigars.   (Street Jewellery)   £25

Figures

The first advertising figures were usually of wood, and stood outside shop frontages. When they finally came in from the cold, to stand in the by now larger and better lit shop windows, they decreased in size and began to be made in other materials, such as metal, plaster, china and papier mâché. Then from the 1930s to the 1950s rubber casting became the most popular, to be replaced later by cheaper plastics.

They are usually simple and uncontroversial in subject, animals and children being challenged only occasionally by the odd historical figure or national stereotype.

Phillips 'Stick a Soles and Heels', rubber advertising figure by Beritex, 12¹/₂in. high. (Sam Weller)   £75

'Puritan Soles', papier mâché figure made by Pytram Ltd for Sir Joseph Caustan & Sons Ltd., Glasgow, 12in. high. (Dave Lewis)   £65

'Moorland Brand Tablets, Make Eating a Real Joy!', papier mâché counter figure, 19in. wide. (Dave Lewis)   £140

Plaster shop display sign for **Invicta Underwear**, 20in. high. (Dave Lewis)   £50

Figures

Wills & Sons Fine Shagg,
painted chalk counter display
sign, 1930's.
(George Court)   £165

'More Hops in Ben Truman'
vulcanized rubber figure on a
wooden base, 17in. high.
(Sam Weller)   £65

Shop window display figure for
**Askeys 'The name for Wafer
Biscuits of Good Taste'**,
produced by **Pytram Ltd, New
Malden, Surrey** of papier-
mâché construction, 1930's,
29in. high.
(Dave Lewis)   £200

Raleigh Industries advertising
figure, 1950's, made of painted
plaster.
(George Court)   £250

Figures

Plaster window display figure
for **Facchino ice cream**, 20in.
high. (Dave Lewis)   £120

'Euthymol Tooth Paste',
vulcanized rubber shop counter
figure made by **Hancock,
Corfield and Waller Ltd,
Mitcham**, 8in. high.
(Dave Lewis)   £50

**'Meltonian Shoe Cream &
Dressings'**, vulcanized rubber
counter display figure, 15½in.
high. (Dave Lewis)   £75

**'MacDonald's, Kilty, Cut
Golden Bar'**, tobacco shop
counter figure made of papier
mâché, 17in. high.
(Dave Lewis)   £90

'Sifta Sam, Jolly Good Salt',
vulcanized rubber counter
figure, 16in. high.
(Dave Lewis)   £85

Figures

Figures

Left

Invicta Underwear plaster display figure made by Harris & Sheldon, 22in. high. (Sam Weller) £200

'Hobson's Choice, Feet Plaisters & Powders, Miles of Smiles after using Hobson's Choice, papier mâché counter figure, 13in. high. (Dave Lewis) £75

'If he can say as you can GUINNESS is good for you', china counter display figure by Wiltshaw & Robbins, 9¼in. high. £125

'Sure Shield, Iodised Throat Tablets', papier mâché counter figure, 12½in. high. (Dave Lewis) £75

Right

'My Goodness My Guinness', china counter display sign by Carltonware, Stoke on Trent. (Dave Lewis) £90

1950's, plastic illuminated shop figure for **Robertson's Golden Shred, 'Golly it's Good',** when switched on, the eyes and pot light up, 24in. high. (Dave Lewis) £125

Vulcanized rubber counter figure for **Drambuie**, 16in. high. (Dave Lewis) £45

'Tubby Trex, Better Cooking', vulcanized rubber counter figure made by Bibby & Sons, Liverpool, 16in. high. (Dave Lewis) £70

Flasks

Watson's No 10 Whisky decanter, 22cm. high.   £500

Melrose Highland Whisky by Doulton, 20cm. high.   £500

Doulton Kingsware Coronation flask for George V and Queen Mary June 22nd 1911, 17cm. high.   £150

Melrose Highland Whisky by Doulton, 20cm. high   £450

Sporting Squire Kingsware flask for Dewar's, circa 1909, 21cm. high.   £150

Palmeira House, Brighton, Great Glen Pure Malt Whisky, by Doulton, 37cm. high.   £400

Wake Up and Get to Business, Watsons Scotch Whisky, 23cm. high.   £750

Sunderland Highland Whisky by Grant, Mackay & Co. by Doulton, 17cm. high. £800

Dirty Dick's Famous Wines by Doulton, 23cm. high.   £450

Schweppes blue Green Ginger Wine flask, 34cm. high.   £200

(Cyril Wickham)

Glass Signs

The earliest glass signs were either hand painted on the back of the glass or had letters carved in wood, painted and placed behind the glass. Technology took a leap forward in the 1890s, however, when the Brilliant Signs Company patented new processes which were to keep them in business until 1975.

Fitzpatrick's Iced Soda Drinks, sign with illuminated base, 27in. high, illuminated, 1930's. (Sam Weller)   £75

Framed glass tablet sign for **Batger's Jersey Caramels** manufactured by Burnham & Co., Deptford, 12in. x 18in. (Dave Lewis)   £65

Buttercup Dairy transfer by Tom Curr, 1920's, 22½in. diameter. (Dave Lewis)   £30

Blue Bird Toffee, 'Take the Home Sweet Home', illuminated glass sign, 1950's, 18¼in. x 15¼in. (Dave Lewis)   £90

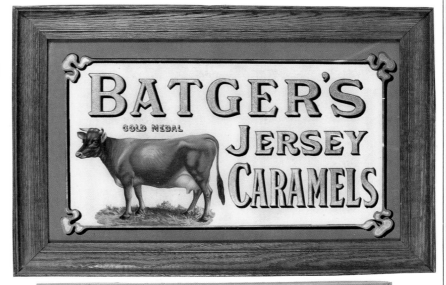

Glassware

Theoretically, glass lent itself just as well as pottery to use as advertising jugs in pubs. In practice, however, it proved less robust, and therefore was less popular with advertisers. After the turn of the century, too, glass jugs became too costly to produce as giveaways. Their resulting rarity has earned them enormous cachet with collectors.

Usher's Whisky decanter, 20cm. high.   £125
Crawford's Finest Very Old Scotch Whisky with enamelled lettering, 13.5cm. high.   £275
Dewar's Whisky, Perth, 50 Gold and Prize Medals, 30cm. high.   £150
'BOS' Whisky as supplied to the House of Lords, 17cm. high.   £275
Bob's Special Old Highland Whisky by R.L. Jones & Co., 19cm. high.   £115
J. & J. McCallum's Perfection Scotch Whisky, 18cm. high. £225
Talbot & Co's Unequalled Mineral Waters, 70 Years Reputation, 18.5cm. high £250
Lawson's Liqueur Whisky, 11cm. high.   £225
Risk's Whisky by Moses Risk & Sons Glasgow, 26cm. high. £150
(Cyril Wickham)

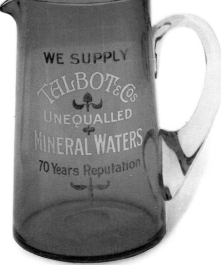

Glassware

Old Grans Special Toddy Scotch Whisky, 10 Years Old, 19cm. high. £115

The Famous 'BOS' Whisky, 11.5cm. high. £275

Catto's V.O.S.H. Whisky decanter, 28cm. high. £150

Teachers Extra Special Whisky, 12cm. high. £125

Mackie's White Horse Cellar, established 1742, 15cm. high. £275

Catto's V.O.S.H. Whisky, Aberdeen, 25cm. high. £150

Robertson's Dundee Whisky, 19cm high. £300

Cantrell & Cochrane's Ginger Ale, acid etched, 18.5cm. high. £225

Drink 'Clova' Whisky, enamelled lettering, 18.5cm. high. £300

Board & Sons Special Irish Whiskey dispenser, 52cm. high. £550
(Cyril Wickham)

Holiday Brochures

By the 1920s and 1930s travel had come within the reach of a major part of the population and travel companies engaged a host of artists to turn out alluring travel posters and brochures to tempt the public. This was the age of the leisured journey, mainly by boat or train, though cycling and motoring were also popular.

Through Scotland by the Caledonian Railway by G. Calthrop.
(Sheffield Railwayana Auctions)
£60

North British, North Eastern and Great Northern Railways Tourist Guide.
(Sheffield Railwayana Auctions)
£60

Deck Plan for the Empress of Britain, 1939. (Yesterday's Paper) £6

Voralpen-Strasse, Munchen-Lindau, 1930's.
(Yesterday's Paper) £3

Canadian Pacific Mont Cruises, 1938.
(Yesterday's Paper) £5

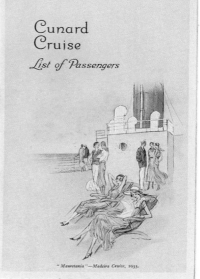

Cunard Cruise, Mauretania, Madeira Cruise, 1933.
(Yesterday's Paper) £5

Holiday Brochures

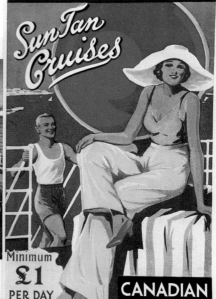

See this Scotland by Steamer Road and Rail, 1931.
(Yesterday's Paper)   £5

Brochure for Bremen and Europa Liners, 1930's.
(Yesterday's Paper)   £8

Sun Tan Cruises by Canadian Pacific, 1930's.
(Yesterday's Paper)   £6

Here's how to see The Broads, display sign, 1960's.
(Sam Weller)   £5

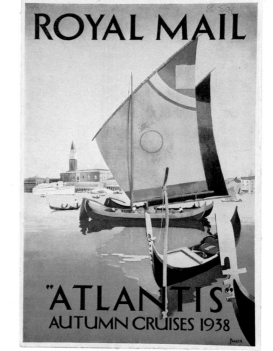

Royal Mail 'Atlantis', Autumn Cruises, 1938.
(Yesterday's Paper)   £6

Labels

Labels are a particularly popular collectable, for they take up very little space, and can be attractively displayed, mounted and framed. They are fragile, of course, and so condition is important when determining value, as is rarity and the product which they advertise.

The labels used on fruit boxes and textile bales are particularly impressive simply because of their size and these are in demand.

Most label collectors however, tend to specialise in such as beer, whisky, perfume, cheese or wine labels, adding to their collections with a keen eye on the weekly shopping, for it is surprising how quickly labels date and acquire a 'period' charm.

Drinks Labels, 1920's–1950's..
(Yesterday's Paper)   £0.50–£2 each

Columbia Belle Apples, label, Wenatchee, Washington, circa 1960, 9in. x 10in.
(Yesterday's Paper)   £3

Lopez Hermanos, cigar box label, 4in. x 4in.
(Yesterday's Paper)   £8

Labels

Chemist and Veterinary labels,
1900–1925.
(Yesterday's Paper)   £2–£5 each

Cheese labels, 1940's–1960.
(Yesterday's Paper)   £0.50–£1 each

Textile labels, 1940's.
(Yesterday's Paper)   £3–£4 each

89

Leaflet Dispensers

The containers for advertising leaflets were usually supplied free by the manufacturer for display at point of sale.

Vetro Mobil, Suspension Filing Equipment, display unit, 1940's.
(Sam Weller)   £48

Printed tin leaflet display **'Of Interest to Cyclists'**, by The County Chemical Co. Ltd., Birmingham, 18in. x 13in. (Dave Lewis)   £85

Letter Racks

Letter Rack produced by J. Thompson, Draper, Grocer and Provision Merchants of Hawes.
(Dave Lewis)   £25

Letter Rack produced by J. Thompson of Hawes.
(Dave Lewis)   £25

Magazine Inserts

In the days before cheap colour printing magazines were invariably printed entirely in black and white. In an attempt to give impact to their products advertisers struck upon the idea of the magazine insert.

These small sheets were printed in bright chromolithographed colours and inserted usually at the back or front of the magazine.

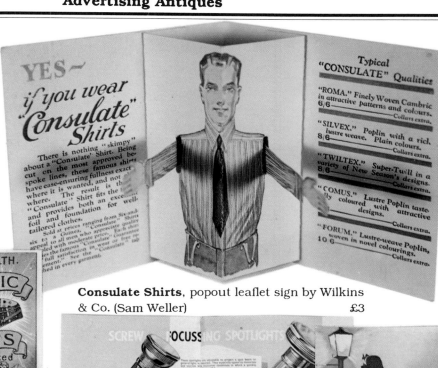

Consulate Shirts, popout leaflet sign by Wilkins & Co. (Sam Weller)   £3

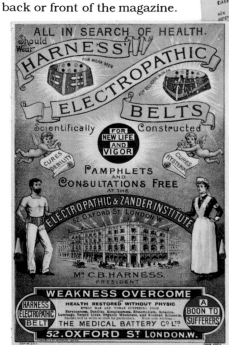

Harness, Electropathic Belts, 1893. (Dave Lewis)   £7

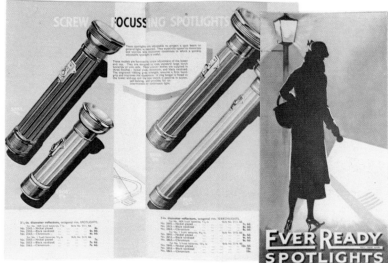

EveryReady Spotlights, leaflet, 1930's. (Sam Weller)   £3

EveryReady, Light wherever you look, leaflet, 1930's. (Sam Weller)   £3

91

Magazine Inserts

Stower's Lime Juice Cordial, 1896. (Dave Lewis) £5

Maypole Soap, 'Dyes All Colours'. (Dave Lewis) £7

Lux, 'This wool shrinking has got to be stopped'. (Yesterday's Paper) £6

Lever Bros Ltd., 'Guess what is under the frying pan'. (Yesterday's Paper) £6

Wright's Coal Tar Soap. (Dave Lewis) £15

Chadwick's Super Six Cord Sewing Cotton, 1878. (Dave Lewis) £7

Lifebuoy Soap, Saves Life. (Yesterday's Paper) £6

Magazine Inserts

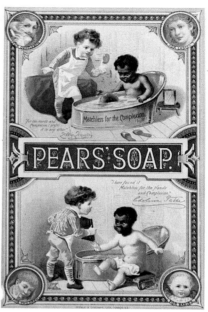

Pears' Soap, 'You Dirty Boy',
1890's.   (Dave Lewis)   £8

Harness, Magnetic Corsets,
1892.   (Dave Lewis)   £7

Pears' Soap, 'Matchless for the
Complexion', 1888.
(Dave Lewis)   £8

Boo-Hoo-Hoo! He's got my
Rowntree's Pastilles.
(Dave Lewis)   £15

Vim, 'A Child can use it'.
(Yesterday's Paper)   £6

Hudson's Soap, 'Make Baby
Smile'.   (Dave Lewis)   £5

Ayer's Hair Vigor, 5in. x 3in.
(Ute Twite)   £5

Magazine Inserts

Liebig Company's Fleisch – Extract,
4in. x 2³/₄in.   (Ute Twite)   £5

The finest perfume is Mikado Cologne,
5in. x 3¹/₄in.   (Ute Twite)   £5

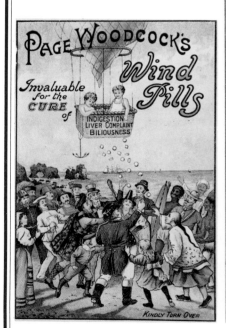

Page Woodcock's Wind Pills,
1899.   (Dave Lewis)   £7

**Suchard's Cocoa, 'Ideas
Competition'.**
(Yesterday's Paper)   £4

**Sunlight Soap, 'Is a Friend in
Need',** 1897.   (Dave Lewis)   £6

Magazine Inserts

Sunlight First!
(Yesterday's Paper)   £6

MERCIFULNESS.

Hudson's Extract of Soap is merciful to the clothes; it only removes the dirt, grease, and stains, leaving the linen behind—spotlessly white, wholesome, and pure.

**Hudson's Soap,
'Mercifulness'.**
(Dave Lewis)   £5

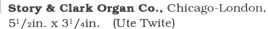

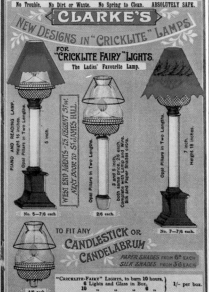

Story & Clark Organ Co., Chicago-London, 5¹/₂in. x 3¹/₄in.   (Ute Twite)   £5

Frazer's Tablets & Frazer's Soap.
(Dave Lewis)   £5

Carter's Lemon Syrup, Dry or Sweet, 1900. (Dave Lewis)   £5

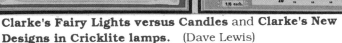

Clarke's Fairy Lights versus Candles and **Clarke's New Designs in Cricklite lamps.** (Dave Lewis)   £7

Magazine Inserts

The Woolson Spice Co.
(Ute Twite)   £5

Lifebuoy Soap.
(Yesterday's Paper)   £6

Sunlight Soap, 'Makes Washing Play'. (Yesterday's Paper)   £6

Royal Windsor Starch, 1868.
(Dave Lewis)   £6

Ayers Cherry Pectoral cures colds, coughs, 5in. x 3^1/$_4$in.
(Ute Twite)   £6

Sunlight Soap, a child can use it. (Lyle)   £6

C. H. Knorr's Nahrungsmittelfabriken,
2^3/$_4$in. x 4^1/$_4$in. (Ute Twite)   £3

Linde's Essenz Fur Kaffee, 2^3/$_4$in. x 4^1/$_4$in.
(Ute Twite)   £3

Magazine Inserts

Sunlight Soap.
(Yesterday's Paper)   £6

Clarke's Pyramid Night Lamp.
(Dave Lewis)   £5

Edward's Harlene.
(Dave Lewis)   £7

Bergers Germania Cacao, 5in.
x 3^1/$_4$in. (Ute Twite)   £5

Aechie Linde's Kaffee Wurze,
2^3/$_4$in. x 4^1/$_4$in. (Ute Twite)   £3

**Plantol Soap, 'Made from Fruit
& Flowers'.** (Yesterday's Paper) £6

**Bar Lock, 'The Typewriter
Company Ltd'**, 1899.   £6

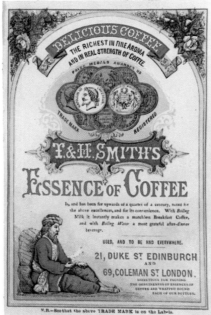

**T. & H. Smith's Essence of
Coffee**, 1868. (Dave Lewis)   £6

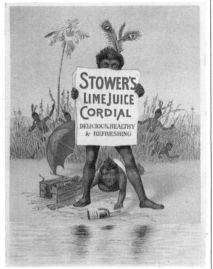

Stower's Lime Juice Cordial,
1896. (Dave Lewis)   £5

Match Strikers

Before the widespread use of matches in boxes there were numerous little containers designed to house them. Made from a variety of materials including wood, bone, glass, papier mâché, Tunbridgeware, enamel, stone and china, their common feature is a lidless compartment for the matches and a grooved or roughened striking surface.

The most numerous and generally regarded as most appealing specimens are those made of porcelain by the German firm of Conte and Boehme.

Whitbread's Bottled Beers match striker. £150

Portland Whisky match striker. £95

Haigs GlenLeven Old Scotch Whisky match striker. £125

Bass Dogs Head match striker. £150

Caley's Table Waters match striker. £150

White Horse Whisky match striker. £75

Scratch my Back match striker. £150

Whitbread Ale in Bottle match striker. £95

(Cyril Wickham)

Match Strikers

Guinness is Good for you, match striker and ashtray. (Muir Hewitt) £40

Jarvie Old Scotch Whisky match striker. £80

Doulton & Co. Ltd., match striker. £80

Worthingtons India Pale Ale match striker. £45

Chairman match striker. £175

Watson's Blue Band match striker. £125

White Horse match holder and ashtray by Shelley. £100

Barneys Royal Scotch match striker. £95

Salt's Pale Ale match striker. £70

(Cyril Wickham)

Packaging

The packaging of yesteryear is always fascinating. Some products are still half recognisable from their modern counterparts, the distinctive yellow tin of Colman's mustard, for example, or the Ovaltine maid.

Every Ready Spotlight torch, box only, circa 1930's.
(Sam Weller) £2

Mother Seigel's World Famed Curative Syrup, 4¹/₂in. high., early 20th century.
(Sam Weller) £4

Ivelcon by St. Ivel Limited.
(Dave Lewis) £4

Bean's Starch, in blue and white packet, 5¹/₄in. high.
(Sam Weller) £1

Jiffy Dyes made by Drummer Dyes. (Dave Lewis) £5

Temperare Distemper Wall Finish. (Dave Lewis) £4

'The Jerome Spool' Photographic Film.
(Sam Weller) £2

Ibco-Lite, The Safe Nightlight, 6in. wide, war issue.
(Sam Weller) £1

Effervescing Limosine manufactured by Oppenheimer Bros & Co., 7in. high.
(Sam Weller) £9

'Greesoff' by Homepacs Ltd, **Cleans everything in the Kitchen**, 7in. high.
(Sam Weller) £4

The 'Tyne' Hair Restorer prepared by R. Cubey.
(Dave Lewis) £3

Cupal Brand 'Cinnamon and Quinine in Lemon Syrup'.
(Sam Weller) £2

Packaging

Wellington Knife Polish.
(Dave Lewis) £6

'Lavro', The Easy Washing
Powder.
(Dave Lewis) £4

Lynx Distemper, makers H.
Sharp & Sons Ltd., Leeds.
(Dave Lewis) £8

Burdall's 'Fullers Earth'.
(Dave Lewis) £2

'Wizard' Knife Polish by A.F.
Barnett & Co.
(Dave Lewis) £6

Reckitt's Starch.
(Dave Lewis) £5

Cook's 'Lightning' Soap.
(Dave Lewis) £4

Motor Brand Beef & Malt Wine
by Elwen & Son, Sunderland,
10$^{1}/_{2}$in. high.
(Dave Lewis) £10

**Johnson Plastic Printing
Frame**, 5in. wide, 1960's.
(Sam Weller) £1

Goddard's Furniture Cream,
free sample, 1$^{3}/_{4}$in. high.
(Sam Weller) £2

Parkinson's Dusting Powder,
4in. high, 1950's.
(Sam Weller) £1

Robin, The New Starch.
(Dave Lewis) £4

Christmas Candles, printed
cardboard box, circa 1900.
(Sam Weller) £3

Mother Shipton's Soap.
(Dave Lewis) £3

Lifebuoy for Health.
(Dave Lewis) £4

The Bulldog Button Card,
Edwardian.
(Sam Weller) £4

Petrol Pumps

The inspiration for the petrol pump came from America, and they were in use in that country for at least ten years prior to their adoption in Britain. Early American brands included Gilbert & Barker, Bowser and Hammond. Ironically, the first petrol pump in England was not introduced by a petrol company, but instead by the A.A. It was the Hon. Treasurer, Ludwig Schlentheim who proposed that the A.A. instal petrol pumps with their ubiquitous colourful globes such as the ones he had been so impressed with on his travels in the U.S.A.

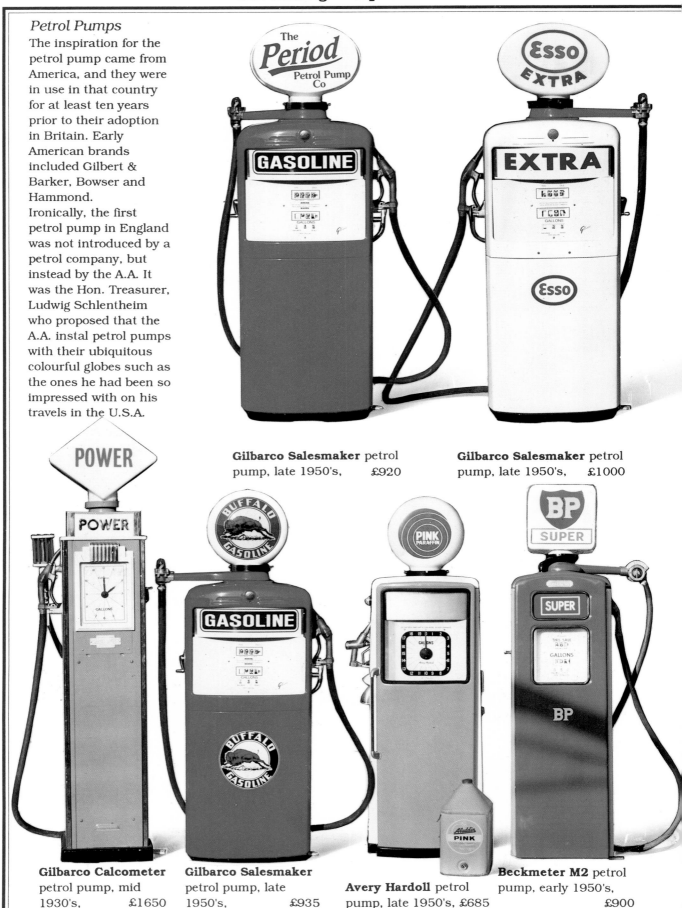

Gilbarco Salesmaker petrol pump, late 1950's, £920

Gilbarco Salesmaker petrol pump, late 1950's, £1000

Gilbarco Calcometer petrol pump, mid 1930's, £1650

Gilbarco Salesmaker petrol pump, late 1950's, £935

Avery Hardoll petrol pump, late 1950's, £685

Beckmeter M2 petrol pump, early 1950's, £900

(The Period Petrol Pump Co.)

Petrol Pumps

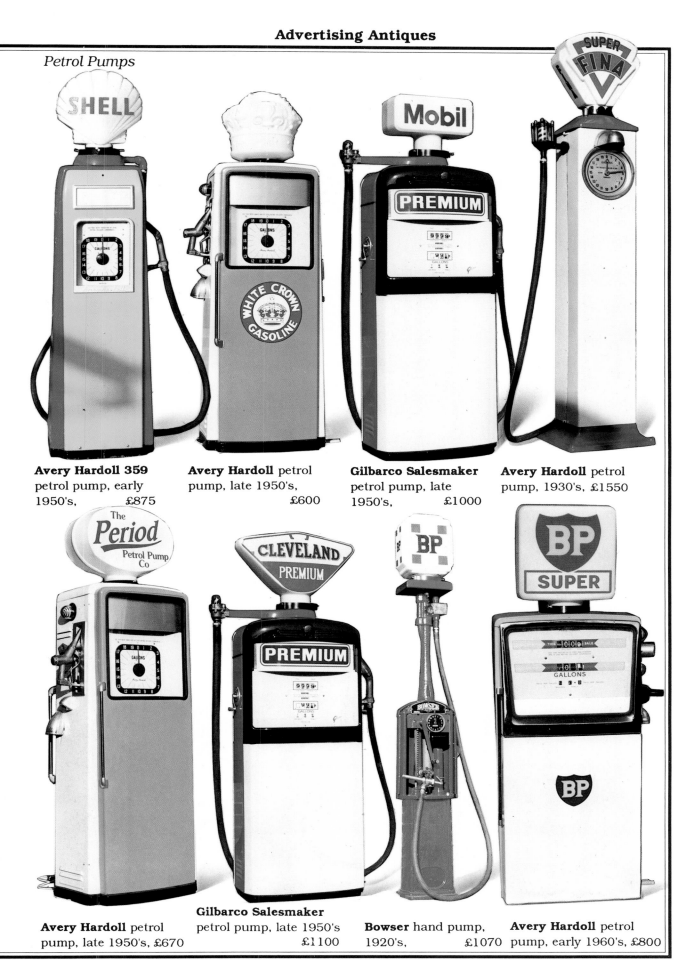

Avery Hardoll 359 petrol pump, early 1950's, £875

Avery Hardoll petrol pump, late 1950's, £600

Gilbarco Salesmaker petrol pump, late 1950's, £1000

Avery Hardoll petrol pump, 1930's, £1550

Avery Hardoll petrol pump, late 1950's, £670

Gilbarco Salesmaker petrol pump, late 1950's £1100

Bowser hand pump, 1920's, £1070

Avery Hardoll petrol pump, early 1960's, £800

(The Period Petrol Pump Co.)

103

Posters

Originally designed to be displayed in public places the function of the poster was to inform by advertising goods or publicising events. Competition in the market place led to a high standard of art work and the production of beautifully coloured and highly decorative items which, unlike some printed collectibles acquiring significance to the collector only with the passing of the years, have been enthusiastically collected since their introduction at the end of the 19th century.

Poster for the **'Worlds Great Snare'** printed by Moodey Bros., Birmingham.
(Dave Lewis)   £60

Ruby Queen and Wang Tia cigarette poster, Geisha Girl, 42in. x 16in.
(Cyril Wickham)   £225

Selo Roll Films, advertising poster, 1930's.
(Sam Weller)   £100

Posters

For Life and Liberty poster, 24in. x 32in. (Cyril Wickham) £150

Nestle's Milk poster, circa 1920. (Yesterday's Paper) £20

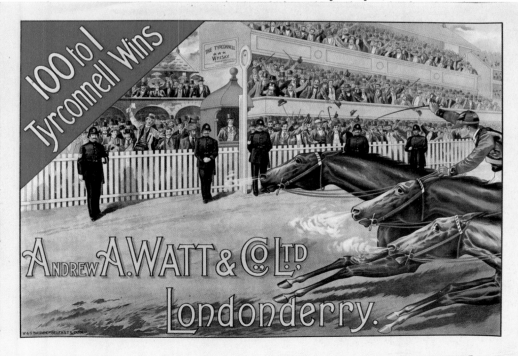

Poster by Andrew A. Watt & Co. Ltd., Londonderry, for **Tyrconnell Whisky**. (Dave Lewis) £95

Posters

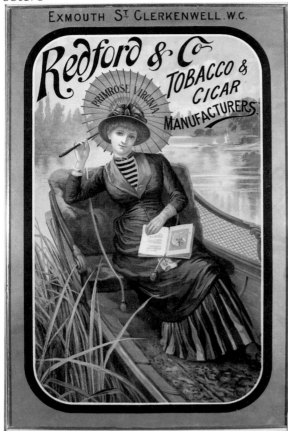

Poster for Redford & Co., Tobacco & Cigar Manufacturers. (Dave Lewis)   £120

Circus Supreme, Sidney Park Cleethorpes, framed poster.
(Cyril Wickham)   £125

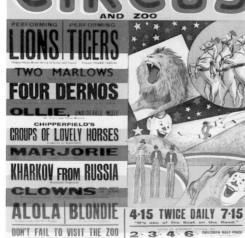

Cody's Circus, framed poster, 24in. x 32in.
(Cyril Wickham)   £125

Lambert & Butler poster for **May Blossom** tobacco and cigarettes. (T. Vennett Smith) £500

Posters

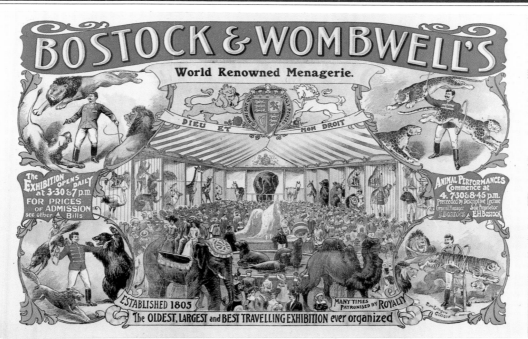

Bostock & Wombwell's World Renowned Menagerie poster, circa 1910.
(Dave Lewis)   £75

**Lithograph poster by B. Minne for the Monaco Grand
Prix**, 1957, 47in. x 31in. (Christie's)   £2000

Geisha girl with Flute, cigarette poster,
42in. x 16in.
(Cyril Wickham)   £225

Printed Tins

American Candy Tins, 1914.
£8 each
Brasso Metal Polish. £5
Double-N liquid grate polish, 5in high, 1920's. £7
The Ivy Burning Oil, The World's Best, 5¼in. high, early 20th century. £22
Victory V Gums for Cold Journeys, printed tin, 7in. wide. £35
Coronation Souvenir presented by **Mrs Walter Fennell**. £15
American Candy Tins, 1914.
£8 each
Quinine & Phosphorus Tablets, printed tin. £2
Palm Oil Shaving Soap in tin container. £6
Pelaw Wax Shoe Polish, printed tin. £2

Liptons Teas, The Finest the World can Produce, printed metal tin by Lipton Ltd., City Road, London, 91.2in. tall. £40
Bisto, For All Meat Dishes, printed tin made by Cerebos Ltd., London, 6in. square. £25
Mennen Talcum For Men, printed tin container, 4in. high. £1
(Sam Weller) (Dave Lewis)

Printed Tins

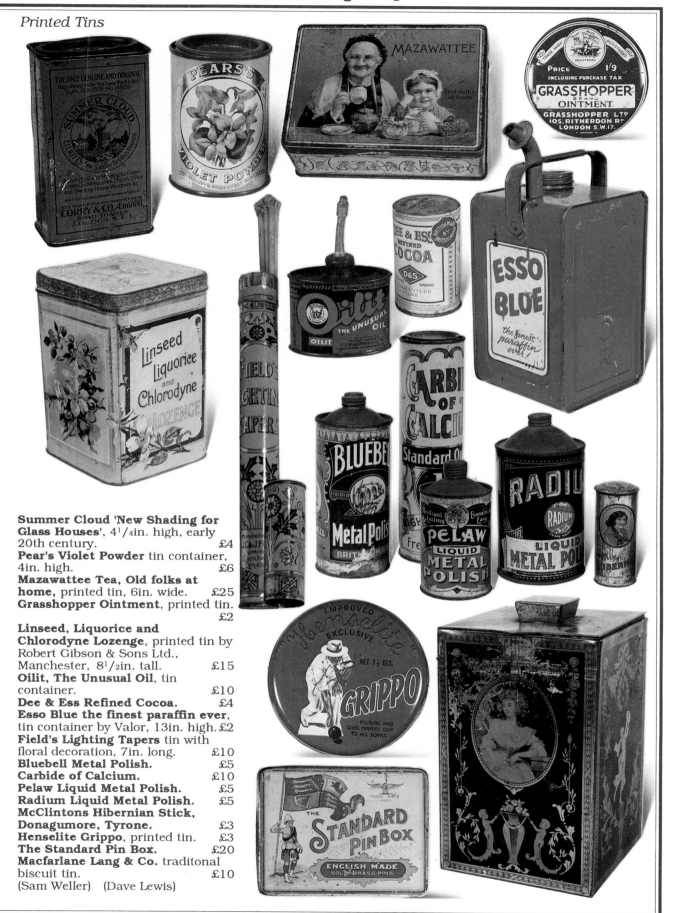

Summer Cloud 'New Shading for Glass Houses', 4¼in. high, early 20th century. £4
Pear's Violet Powder tin container, 4in. high. £6
Mazawattee Tea, Old folks at home, printed tin, 6in. wide. £25
Grasshopper Ointment, printed tin. £2

Linseed, Liquorice and Chlorodyne Lozenge, printed tin by Robert Gibson & Sons Ltd., Manchester, 8½in. tall. £15
Oilit, The Unusual Oil, tin container. £10
Dee & Ess Refined Cocoa. £4
Esso Blue the finest paraffin ever, tin container by Valor, 13in. high. £2
Field's Lighting Tapers tin with floral decoration, 7in. long. £10
Bluebell Metal Polish. £5
Carbide of Calcium. £10
Pelaw Liquid Metal Polish. £5
Radium Liquid Metal Polish. £5
McClintons Hibernian Stick, Donagumore, Tyrone. £3
Henselite Grippo, printed tin. £3
The Standard Pin Box. £20
Macfarlane Lang & Co. traditonal biscuit tin. £10
(Sam Weller)   (Dave Lewis)

Printed Tins

Oxo Cubes, printed tin. £3
Nu-Silver, Plates & Renovates, printed tin, 1950's. £2
F.L.P. To Prevent Rust on Chromium, 2½in. diameter, 1960's. £4
Voltas Wax Polish, printed tin. £3
Carbolic Ointment. £3
Canary Boot Polish, printed tin. £4
Hindoo Pen, printed tin, 1950's. £4
The Laurel, Ladies Boudoir safety razor, 2in. wide. £8
Field's Lighting Tapers tin complete with contents by J.C. & J. Field, Ltd., Lambeth, London, 12in. long. £20
E.J. Riley Ltd., Accrington. £20
Boothroyds printed tin needle container, 2¼in. high, early 20th century. £5
McVities & Price's Biscuits. £15
Cadbury's Cocoa. £10
Coronation of George V and Queen Mary. £15
Pine Tree Lozenges. £5
Jester Wax Shoe Polish, printed tin. £8
Standing's Noted Teas. £3
Indian Cerate Family Ointment, prepared by Parkinsons Chemists, Burnley, printed tin, 7in. wide. £20
Slippery Elm Food for Infants, prepared by Dr. Thompson Pure Food Co., printed tins, 2lbs nett, 1lb & ½lb. £10, £8, £6
Harrogate Health Salt, for the stomach, liver and kidneys, printed tin, 4in. high. £15

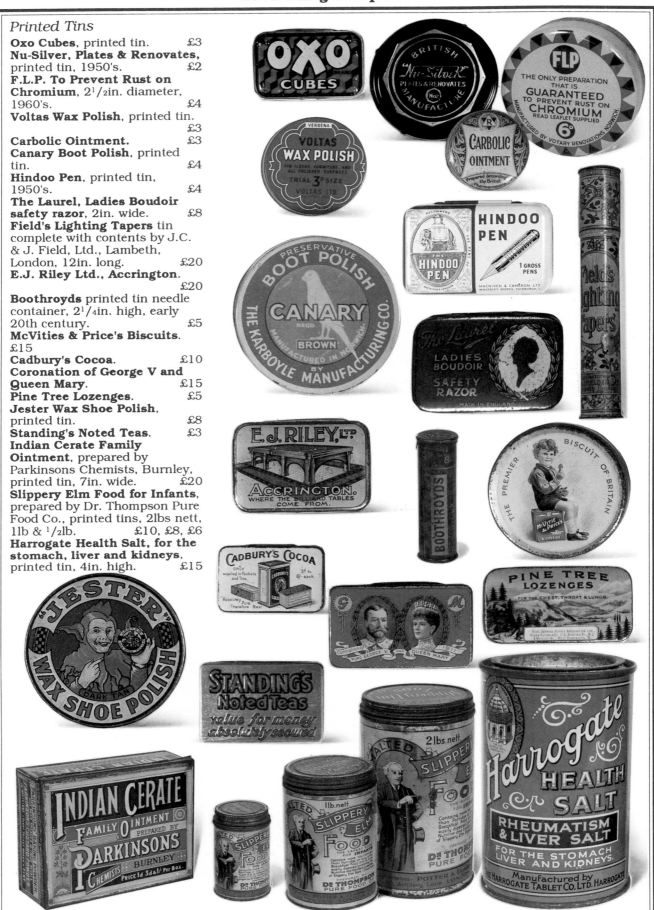

(Dave Lewis)   (Sam Weller)

Pub Jugs

Though ceramic and glass jugs have been in use in taverns and inns for hundreds of years, it was only in the mid 19th century, when different brands of whisky began to be bottled, that the distillers latched on to the idea of offering free water jugs advertising their own particular blends. Between 1870 and the outbreak of war in 1914, Scotch Whisky became established as a hugely popular and socially acceptable drink not only in England but throughout the Empire, and indeed the world.

Simonds of Reading Pale Ale by James Green & Nephew Ltd., London, 15cm. high. £200

Ross's Sparkling Grape Fruit by Grays Pottery, Stoke on Trent, 11cm. high. £150

Huntly Blend Scotch Whisky by Palissy, 10cm. high. £150

Cobbold's Lancer Whisky, 14cm. high. £350

Ballantyne Whisky by M.P. Bell & Co., 22cm. high. £575

Macnair Twinkle Scotch Whisky by Doulton, 17cm. high. £375

Hunt's Pure Cider on draught and in bottle by Longpark, Torquay, 15cm. high. £175

G.W. Villar Cash Trader jug, 18cm. high. £375

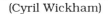
(Cyril Wickham)

Pub Jugs

Worthington's in Bottle, Oldest Burton Brewers, manufactured by Copeland & Sons, Stoke on Trent, 16.5cm. high. £800

Offiler's Special Reserve Whisky by Shelley, 15cm. high. £350

John Begg's Scotch Whisky by Fielding, 14cm. high. £375

Dew of Killarney Irish Whiskey by Port Dundas Potters, 16cm. high. £350

Buchanan's Black & White Whisky, Polo Player by Frank Beardmore & Co., 17cm. high. £450

Corbett's Irish Whiskey by D.A. Campbell, Belfast, 20cm. high. £250

Watson's No. 10 Scotch Whisky attributed to Shelley, 17cm. high. £350

Blue Bell Scotch Whisky by Nederkind & Co., London, 15cm. high. £425

Teachers Highland Cream, Bury the Corkscrew, 16cm. high. £425

Henry White & Co's Red Heart Rum by Frank Beardmore, Fenton, 16cm. high. £450

(Cyril Wickham)

Pub Jugs

Uamvar Famous Whisky by Innes & Grieve Ltd., manufactured by Copeland, 13cm. high. £450

Grant's 'Stand Fast' Whisky by James Green & Nephew, 8.5cm. high. £125

R. & H. Jenner & Sons, A quart of ale is a dish for a king by Doulton, 16.5cm. high. £400

Black Friar Gin by Dartmouth Pottery, 17cm. high. £125

Grant's Invercauld Scotch, 15cm. high £500

Greenlee Brothers Claymore Scotch Whisky by Royal Doulton, 16.5cm. high. £450

Courage's Famous Beers, 14cm. high. £250

Worthington, Coronation of George V and Queen Mary June 22 1911, 12.5cm. high. £175

Ainslie's Whisky, Edinburgh Castle and National Gallery by Copeland, 10cm. high. £350

Buchanan's Black & White Whisky by Frank Beardmore, Fenton, 17cm. high. £750

(Cyril Wickham)

Pub Jugs

Slater Rodgers Thistle Whisky by Ch. Kennedy, Glasgow, 19cm. high.   £550
Henley's Devonshire Cyder, Newton Abbot by Longpark, Torquay, 15cm. high.   £175
Rogers 31 Honours, London 1912–1933 by Pountney & Co., 12cm. high.   £200
Barnsley Brewery Co., Famous for mild and bitter ales by Doulton, 17cm. high.   £750
White Horse Whisky by Shelley, 14cm. high.   £200
Isleworth Special Old Whiskies, 17cm. high.   £250
R. & H. Jenner, Southwark, London, 1904 by Doulton, 16½cm. high.   £450
Watson's Old Scotch Whisky, manufactured by Doulton, 14½cm. high   £500
Robbie Burns Famed Old Scotch Whisky, by R.H. Thomson & Co., Leith, 14cm. high.   £450
Watson's Blue Band Whisky attributed to Shelley, 16cm. high.   £450
(Cyril Wickham)

Pub Jugs

Whitbread's Stag, 15cm. high.
£125

John Haig's GlenLeven by Fielding, Stoke on Trent, 9¹/₂cm. high. £300

Encore Scotch Whisky by Cranston & Elliot Ltd., Edinburgh, 16¹/₂cm. high. £325

Morgan Lloyd & Son GlenLivet Whisky by Price, Bristol, 17cm. high. £650

Greer's Scotch Whisky, Age and Quality Guaranteed, 15cm. high. £200

Black & White Whisky, two dogs by Shelley, 12cm. high.
£175

Watson's No. 10, treacleglaze, Bay of Naples, 16¹/₂cm. high.
£500

Banks's Noted Ales, Park Brewery, Wolverhampton, 12cm. high. £400

Georges' Beers by Pountney & Co., 10cm. high. £200

Buchanan's Black & White Whisky, Eagle, 17cm. high.
£750

(Cyril Wickham)

Pub Jugs

Bass & Co., Pale Ale, 1837-1897, Queen Victoria commemorative, 17cm. high.
£600

Bobs Whisky (Best Old Blended Scotch), 14cm. high.
£375

Dunville's Special Liqueur Whisky by D.A. Campbell, Belfast, 13¹/₂cm. high. £150

Allsops Coronation Jug, 17¹/₂cm. high. £550

Mackie's White Horse Whisky Refuse Cheap Imitations, 15cm. high. £550

M.B. Foster & Sons, London, Bugle ale & stout, 17cm. high. £800

Buchanan's Special Red Seal Scotch Whisky, 19cm. high. £800

Dandie Dinmont Special Whisky by A. Alexander, Leith, 15cm. high. £450

Greyhound Special Scotch Whisky by Fielding, 11¹/₂cm. high £225

Schweplet, Schweppes Table Waters, 11¹/₂cm. high. £175
(Cyril Wickham)

Pub Jugs

McNish's Doctors Special Whisky, 19¹/₂cm. high. £550

Burke's Dublin Whiskey by Fielding, 15¹/₂cm. high. £350

Meynell Hunt Fine Old Scotch Whisky by Alton & Co. Ltd., Wardwick, Derby, 16cm. high. £450

Wright & Greig's Roderick Dhu Old Highland Whisky, 14cm. high. £350

Watson's of Dundee No 10 Whisky, 19cm. high. £750

Simpson's Scotch Whisky by Doulton, 15cm. high. £400

Marston's Burton Ales by T.G. Green & Co., 11¹/₂cm. high. £175

Johnnie Walker Whisky, manufactured by Doulton, 15¹/₂cm. high. £500

R. & H. Jenner & Sons, Coronation 1911 by Royal Doulton, 16¹/₂cm high. £450
(Cyril Wickham)

Rowntrees Labels

The history of Rowntree's begins in 1862 when Henry Rowntree bought out the cocoa side of Samuel Tuke's grocery business in Walmgate, York. Joseph Rowntree joined his brother in 1869 and by 1873 the firm had expanded into chocolate confectionery. The company merged with the Mackintosh company in 1969 and was taken over by Nestle Ltd. in 1988. The original proprietors were staunch Quakers, and the firm was noted for its welfare schemes and schools.

Rowntree's Homeopathic Cocoa label, 8in. x 12in.
£25

Rowntree's Assorted Chocolates label, 7in. x 10in. £15

Rowntree's Orange Fruit Creams, label, 6in. x 9in.
£10

Rowntree's Windsor Mixture label, 7in. x 13in.
£12

(Yesterday's Paper)

Rowntrees Labels

Rowntree & Co Liquorice Creams,
label, 7in. x 10in.   £10
Rowntree's Ping Pong Biscuits label,
8in. x 12in.   £25
Rowntree's Assorted Fruit Creams,
label, 8in. x 11in.   £10
Rowntree's Bouquet Creams, label,
8in. x 10in.   £10
(Yesterday's Paper)

Showcards

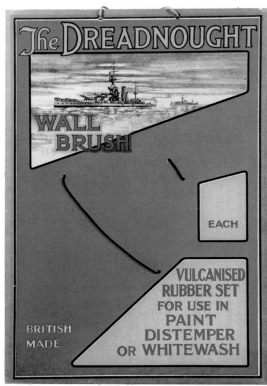

Showcards began to be popular in the 1880s when chromolithography had developed to such a stage that reproduction of a picture rivalled oil painting in quality.

By 1897 the colour printers Mardon, in Bristol, were employing scores of in-house artists, many of whom chalked and stippled the stones for twelve or more colours for one showcard. They also adapted their box die cutting processes to shape these cards.

In the early decades of the 20th century four-colour lithography and the rotary press came in to supplant traditional chromolithographic techniques, with much duller results. Thereafter the showcard declined in quality and popularity, as advertisers latched on to different advertising gimmicks.

Bovril for Health & Strength, printed card sign, 16in. x 22in.
(Dave Lewis)   £120
The Dreadnought Wall Brush, display card, 15in. high. circa First World War, brush not attached
(Sam Weller).   £10
An HP Quality Product showcard, 11in. x 9in.
(Sam Weller)   £5

Showcards

Printed tinplate showcard for
Mansion Polish, 7¹/₂in. x 9¹/₂in.
(Sam Weller)   £18

Co-operative Union Ltd, display sign,
circa 1920/30's.
(Sam Weller)   £15

Printed card counter display sign for
'Vesta Paints for every home', 21¹/₂in.
high. (Lyle)   £25

Zon Sun Bathing Oil makes you a
Glorious Brown, showcard, 12³/₄in. x
9¹/₂in., 1930's. (Sam Weller)   £30

121

Showcards

Printed showcard for **Fry's Milk Chocolate**, 19in. x 12in. (Dave Lewis)   £60

'Player's Number 3', plastic coated showcard, 7¹/₂in. x 9¹/₂in., 1950's. (Sam Weller) £30

Counter display sign for **'Fields Pure Toilet Soap, Keeps you in the Pink of Health'**, 10in. high. (Dave Lewis)   £15

Printed showcard for **Oxo, It's "Meat and Drink" to you**, late 1920's. (Lyle)   £40

Tin sign for **C.& J. Clark manufacturers of Boots, Shoes & Slippers**, 20in x 16in. (Dave Lewis)   £75

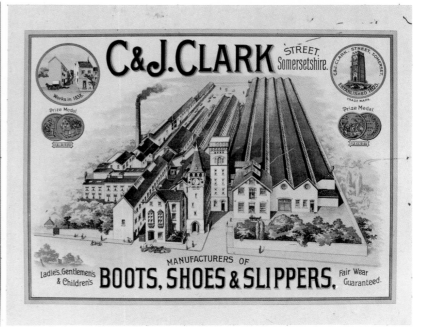

Showcards

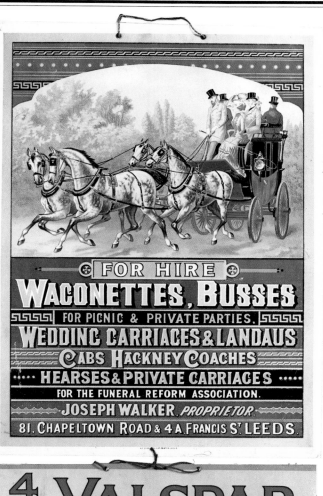

Exide Battery display sign, 1930's.
(Sam Weller)   £2
Printed showcard for **Joseph Walker,
Wagonettes & Busses** produced by Alf
Cooke, Card Colour Printers, Leeds.
(Dave Lewis)   £85
**Ransomes 'Ace' Ball Bearing Lawn
Mower**, showcard, 19in. high.
(Sam Weller)   £20
1930's **Valspar Enamels and Varnish**,
hanging display card, 14in. x 19in.
(Lyle)   £20

Showcards

Printed card sign in original frame for **Jacob & Co's Water Biscuits**. (Dave Lewis) £120

Die-cut Edwardian **'Euthymol Cold Cream, Protects in Winter or Summer'** , counter display sign, 10in. high. (Dave Lewis) £45

1930's cardboard die-cut shop display sign for **'Whiteway's Cydrax, Cyder's Little Sister'**, 29in. high. (Dave Lewis) £65

1930's **Liquid Lino** counter display card with folding stand, 15in. x 25in. (Lyle) £20

Showcards

Oxygen Straw Cleaner hanging showcard, 13in. wide.
(Sam Weller)   £15

Daddies Favourite Sauce, display sign, 1940's.   (Sam Weller)   £35

Murray's Mixture, The Ideal Pipe Tobacco, printed counter sign, 7¹/₂in. x 5³/₄in.
(Sam Weller)   £6

Printed showcard for **Berry's Blacking**, 11in. x 17in.   (Dave Lewis)   £45

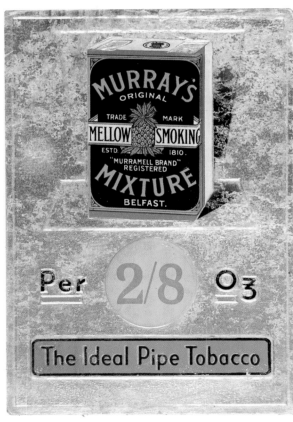

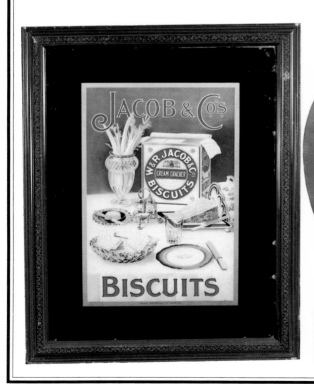

Showcards

Left

Printed showcard for **Ridgways Coffee**, 20in. x 13in.
(Dave Lewis) £85

Printed showcard for **Colman's Starch**, 9in. x 14in.
(Dave Lewis) £60

Framed printed card sign for **Jacob & Co's Biscuits**, 24in. x 28in.
(Dave Lewis) £95

'Andrews Liver Salt' showcard, 11½in. x 9¾in. (Dave Lewis) £35

Right

T.D. Cross & Sons Ltd., 'Free Wheels', showcard 9¾in. x 11½in., 1960's (Sam Weller) £8

Phillips' Dental Magnesia, printed cardboard display sign, 29in. long.
(Sam Weller) £8

Printed card sign for **Yorkshire Relish, 'The Most Delicious Sauce in The World'**, circa 1890, 21in. x 30in. (Dave Lewis) £200

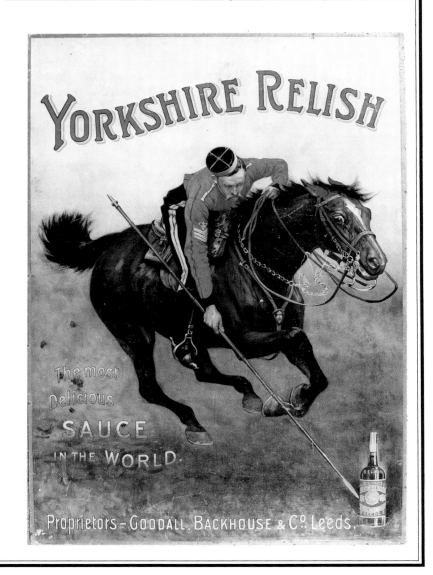

Showcards

Chiltonian Biscuits, **'Their ready sale ensures absolute freshness'**, counter showcard, 25in. high. (Sam Weller) £48

The **'Kilner' Jar** showcard, 14¹/₂in. x 9in., post-war. (Sam Weller) £8

Greensmith's Derby Dog Biscuits, showcard, 18in. x 24in., early 20th century. (Sam Weller) £100

Co-operative Union Ltd display sign **'Mutual Trust that is Co-operation'**, 1930's. (Sam Weller) £15

Showcards

Printed showcard for **Colman's Starch**, 17in. x
13in.   (Dave Lewis)   £50

Printed showcard for **Bovril** by Tom Purvis,
1920's.   (Yesterday's Paper)   £40

Ransome's 'Leo' and 'Cub' Lawn Mowers,
showcard, 18in. high.   (Sam Weller)   £20

Mascot showcard, 14in. x 9¹/₂in.
(Sam Weller)   £5

Showcards

'Golden Shred, The Family Favourite', printed die-cut card display sign, 11in. high. (Dave Lewis) £35

Printed showcard for **Buchanan's Delicious Home Made Marmalade** produced by Forrest & Son, Argyle Street, Glasgow, 25in. x 30in. (Dave Lewis) £200

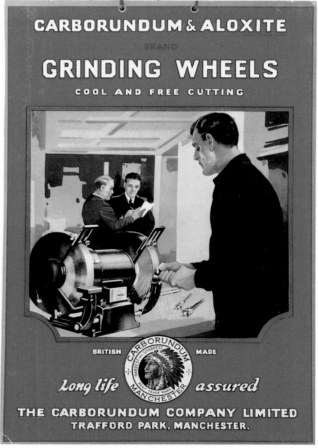

Printed card for **Elliman's Embrocation** framed by Wm. Strain & Sons, Belfast, 25in. x 15in. (Dave Lewis) £75

Carborundum & Aloxite Grinding Wheels, showcard, 13in. x 9in. (Sam Weller) £15

Showcards

Printed card sign for **The Celebrated Yorkshire Relish prepared only by Goodall Backhouse & Co., Leeds**, 15in. x 20in. (Dave Lewis) £65

Maison Lyons Chocolates, A gift worth giving for the joy it gives', 1920's, printed showcard. (Lyle) £30

1930's printed showcard for **Cephos, The Safe and Certain Cure**. (Lyle) £15

Printed card sign for **Sallyco Mineral Water Co., Hornsey**, 20in. x 15^1/$_2$in. (Dave Lewis) £85

Style Catalogues

From the mail order and shop catalogues of the last thirty years one obtains an instant and vivid impression of taste and design prevailing at the time of their publication. Some of the names on these have already become legends and are now highly collectable ephemera with a strong pull of instant nostalgia, as are the clothes, furniture etc. which they illustrate.

The most sought after of all are Biba catalogues, posters etc. perhaps because the company is now long gone, and because more than all the others it epitomises the mood of the 60s and early 70s. Others, such as Habitat, Laura Ashley and Next are still with us and provide the best examples of style in the 70s and 80s. Not only their contents, but also the design of the brochures themselves are of interest, and are beginning to appeal to collectors of social history.

Biba Mail Order forms and
letterhead.
(Street Jewellery)   £10

Style Catalogues

Barbara Hulanicki, the daughter of a Polish diplomat, came to the UK in 1948 and opened her first Art Deco Biba shop in 1964. This was to promote the look that made Twiggy famous, and became the first superstore of style, patronised by rock stars and shop girls alike. Derry & Tom's in Kensington High Street was transformed into the Big Biba with a 1930s Rainbow Room, exotic Kasbah and an all over style of chic Art Deco black. Branches were opened all over the world. However, the firm crashed in 1975. Hulanicki then went to Brazil, where she set up a boutique in Sao Paolo, before returning briefly to the UK and then settling in Miami.

Biba Mail Order catalogues 1967–69.
(Street Jewellery)   £25 each

Style Catalogues

Habitat was the 1960s brainchild of Terence Conran, and sold entire ensembles of homewares to young professional people who wanted watered down modernism married to natural unadorned materials. Their first catalogue, published in 1964, was a huge success, and the new style blew down the High Street of the time like a breath of fresh air. By the 80s however, their popularity had waned and in 1989 Conran sought to amalgamate it with Mothercare and BHS into the Storehouse Group.

Style Catalogues

Habitat Mail Order catalogues 1969–89.

(Street Jewellery)

£10–25 each

Style Catalogues

1993 marks the 40th anniversary of the company Laura Ashley started with her husband by designing tea towels and printing them on the kitchen table in their Pimlico home. They were snapped up like hot cakes on the King's Road, and the Ashleys quickly realised that their designs were potential winners. They moved to Laura's native Wales, where they opened their first shop and sewing room in 1963 in Llanidloes. The rest, as they say, is history.

The first Ashley catalogue appeared around 1978, and mail order soon became a major part of the business too. The Ashleys moved to France, where they had a chateau, for tax reasons, and Laura died in 1986 after a fall in her daughter's home.

Laura Ashley Home Furnishings 1981

Style Catalogues

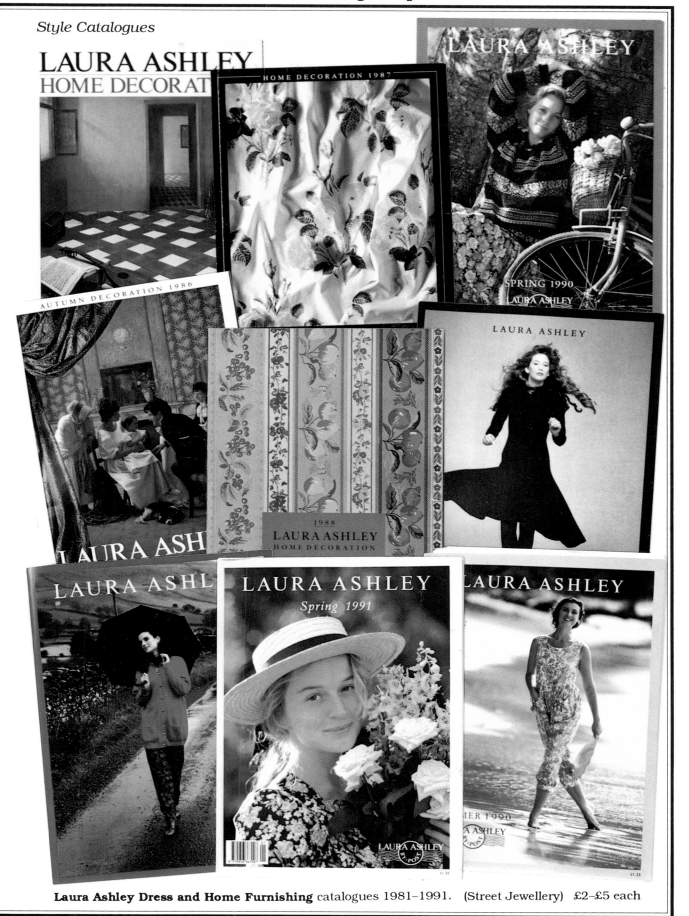

Laura Ashley Dress and Home Furnishing catalogues 1981–1991.   (Street Jewellery)   £2–£5 each

Style Catalogues

The first Next stores were opened in February 1982 by George Davis, and over 400 branches sprang up over the next four years, catering for the 20+ age group.

Next Interior Mail Order catalogue 1985/86.
(Street Jewellery)   £5

Next for Autumn Winter 1985.
(Street Jewellery)   £5

Next Directory, 1st Edition 1986/7.
(Street Jewellery)   £15

Style Catalogues

Janet Reger set up in business in 1967, designing and producing silk lingerie for the very top of the market, at £300 for a bra and knickers, to over £1,000 for a negligee. The company failed in 1987 however with debts of over £1 million and Reger sold her name and went to work for Berlei. She has since rebuilt her business, though on a much smaller and less flamboyant scale.

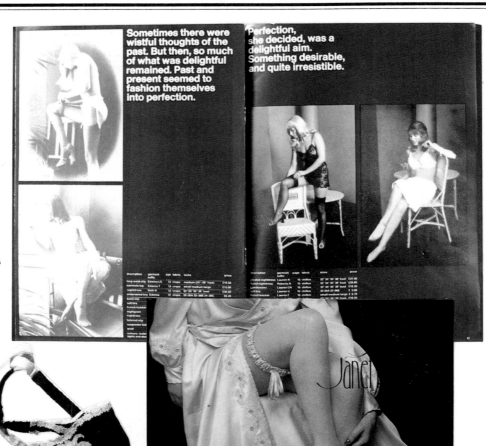

Sometimes there were wistful thoughts of the past. But then, so much of what was delightful remained. Past and present seemed to fashion themselves into perfection.

Perfection, she decided, was a delightful aim. Something desirable, and quite irresistible.

Janet Reger catalogue 1970's.
(Yesterday's Paper)   £12

Janet Reger Mail Order catalogue, 1978.   (Street Jewellery)   £10

Tinplate Signs

Comparatively little is known about the development of tinplated signs or their producers, as few were signed or have a maker's mark. They were used almost exclusively indoors, as they lacked the robustness of enamel and could not withstand damp. They had the advantage, however, that they could be printed with fine detail, which could withstand close inspection.

Few have survived in good condition and most of these are finger plates or shelf edgings, retained because of their functional qualities.

Left

Printed tin sign for **Thomson's Manures, The Result of Many Years Practical Experience'**, 18in. x 12in.. £50

Printed tin embossed sign for **Acme Wringers**, 8in. x 16in. £45

Printed tin sign for **Wellsaline Super Lubricants** produced by Matthew Wells & Co. Ltd., Manchester, 16in. x 21in. £65

Right

Shield shaped printed metal sign for **Hill, Evans & Co's, Pure Malt Vinegar**. £20

Printed tin sign for **Aspinall's Enamel Ltd., Varnish Works, Mitcham, Surrey**. £15

Printed tin hanging sign for **Solid Gold Grapevine Cigarettes** by B. Morris & Sons Ltd. £15

Printed tin sign for **Tennent's Zuiver Light Beer**, 13in. x 19in. £50

Chemico embossed tin sign produced for the **County Chemical Co. Ltd., Chemico Works, Birmingham**, 17in. x 21in. £100

(Dave Lewis)

Tinplate Signs

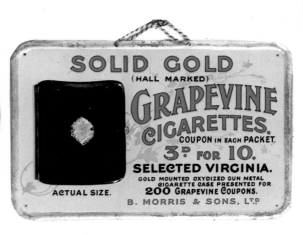

Tinplate Signs

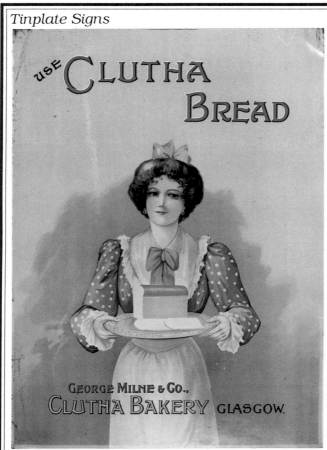

Clutha Bread printed tin sign manufactured by
Charles Lightowler, Hunsley, Leeds.   £60

Printed tin sign for **Titan Patent Soap,
Absolutely No Rubbing**.   £85

Tin sign for **Pelaw liquid metal polish, Easy
and lasting**, 13in. x 19in.   £120

Embossed tin hanging sign for **A. Sommerville
& Co's 'Bremer Börsen Feder'**.   £20
(Dave Lewis)

Tinplate Signs

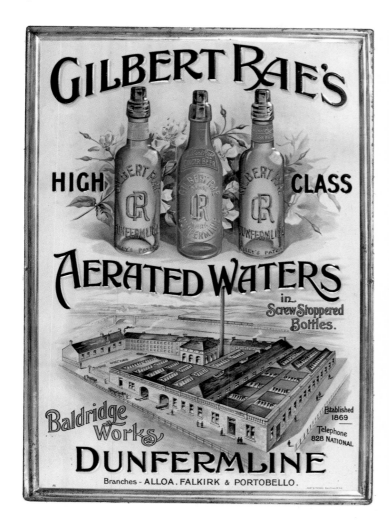

Embossed tin sign for **Gilbert Rae's Aerated Waters** made by Hunt & Frenkel, Blackfriars Road, London. £200

Printed tin sign for **Sandy McDonald, Special Liqueur Scotch Whisky**, 6in. x 13in. £20

Printed tin sign for **Fairy Soap** produced by Thomas Hedley & Co. Ltd., Newcastle-upon-Tyne, printed by Charles Lightowler, Hunsley, Leeds. £85

(Dave Lewis)

Tinplate Signs

Left
'Drink Vigoral, A Foe to Fatigue' embossed tin sign made by Kaufmann & Strauss Co., N.Y., 7in. x 11in.
(Dave Lewis) £45
'Fisons Granular Vegerite', tinplate showcard, 5³/₄in. x 9in.
(Sam Weller) £10
Printed tin sign for **The Clan Mackenzie Scotch Whisky** with calendar, 10in. x 7in.
(Dave Lewis) £20
Printed tin sign for **Cameo Boot Polish**.
(Dave Lewis) £15

Right
Pressed tin sign for **E. & J. Burke stout, 'First in the Field'**, 16in. x 23in.
(Dave Lewis) £75
Printed tin sign for **Barr's Scotch Ginger Beer**, 18in. x 25in.
(Dave Lewis) £85
Embossed tin sign for **John Haig's Glenleven Whisky**, 17in. x 25in.
(Dave Lewis) £120
Player's Please tinplate sign, 28in. high.
(Sam Weller) £25

Tinplate Signs

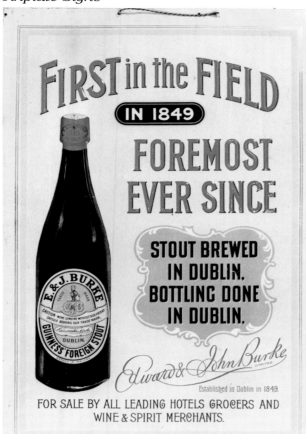

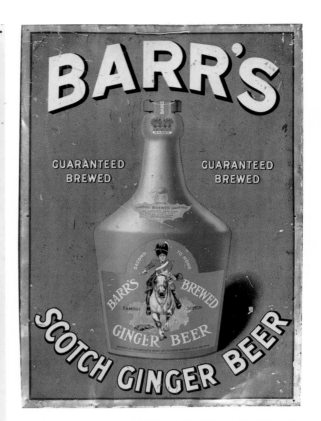

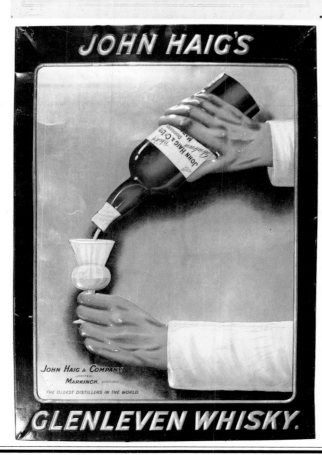

Tinplate Signs

Embossed tin sign for **Gallaher's 'War Horse' Tobacco** produced by Gallaher Ltd., 20in. x 14in. £130

Printed tin sign for **McNee's High Class Jams & Jellies**. £20

Embossed tin sign for **John Haig's Glenleven Whisky**. £100

Printed tin sign for **Turnbull's Standard Scotch Whisky**, made by McCaw Stevenson & Orr, Glasgow. £60

(Dave Lewis)

Tinplate Signs

Embossed tin sign for
**Glovers Washing
Preparations**, 9¹/₂in. x
14in. £45

Printed tin sign for
Stenhouse Liqueur Whisky
produced by Wm.
Stenhouse & Co., Glasgow,
London & Manchester. £45

Tin sign for **'Comet, The
All-Star Comic'** featuring
**Buck Jones, Fighting
Sheriff of the Ranges.** £45
(Dave Lewis)

Toffee Tins

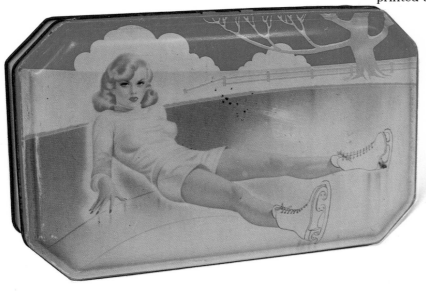

Left

Cremona Toffee Tin, 1929, North East Coast Exhibition. (Street Jewellery) £15
Nutjoy Toffee tin. (Street Jewellery) £10
'Devon Cream Toffee', printed tin by **Radiance, Toffee Works, Doncaster**, 6in. high. (Dave Lewis) £25
Thornes, Assorted Toffee, Standard Almond, Brazil and Mint, printed tin, 1930's. (Muir Hewitt) £10
Printed tin depicting a glamorous ice skater, by **George W. Horner & Co. Ltd., Chester le Street, Durham**, 8in. wide.
(Dave Lewis) £10
Maynards Ltd Perfection, printed tin, 8in. high. (Dave Lewis) £20

Right

Blue Bird Toffee, Captain Bones, Hys Treasure, printed tin by Harry Vincent Ltd. (Lyle) £15
Imperial Toffee by C E Taylor & Co. Ltd., Harrogate. (Dave Lewis) £10
Dainty Dinah Mixed Toffees by George W. Horner & Co. Ltd., in printed peacock tin. (Lyle) £10
Thorne's Extra Super Creme Toffee in a souvenir tin from The British Empire Exhibition, Wembley, 1924. (Lyle) £20
'Whipped Cream Toffee', printed tin by Turner & Wainwrights, Brighouse, Yorkshire, 6in. high. (Dave Lewis) £25
Mixed Dainty Dinah Toffees by Horner. (Dave Lewis) £15
'Thorne's Extra Super Creme Toffee', printed tin, souvenir of The British Empire Exhibition, 1924. (Dave Lewis) £20
Thorne's Extra Super Creme Toffee, printed tin, 15in. high. (Dave Lewis) £20

Toffee Tins

Trade Catalogues

Trade Catalogues were published for all sorts of products from the most humble to the exotic. They provide a fascinating insight into the life of the times, what products and innovations were on offer, and how much they cost.

As they were the shop window for most firms they are generally of fine quality printing, sometimes in full colour, on good quality paper.

Their value is usually dictated by the popularity of the objects they portray, those for toys, fishing tackle, tools, furniture, clothing, china and the like, are highly prized while those for such as 'Rainwater Heads' have limited appeal.

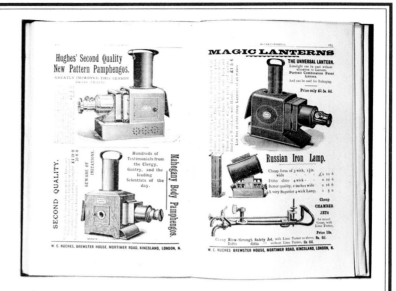

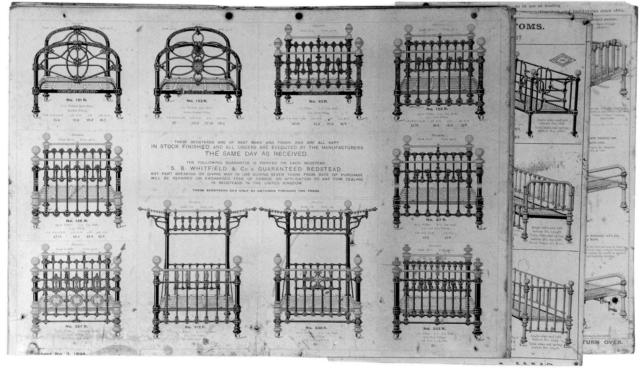

Trade Catalogues

Left

Magic Lantern Manual by An Expert, 1893.
(Lyle) £25

S.B. Whitfield and Co. Guaranteed Bedsteads.
(Sam Weller) £25

Hillman Super Minx and **Morris 1100** brochures, 1962.
(Yesterday's Paper) £5 each

Dinky Toys catalogue No. 6.
(Jim Binns) £8

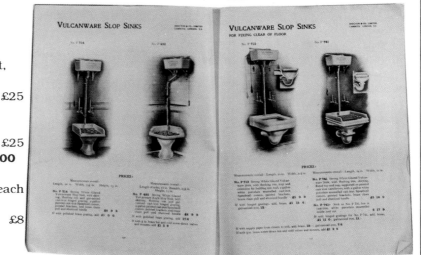

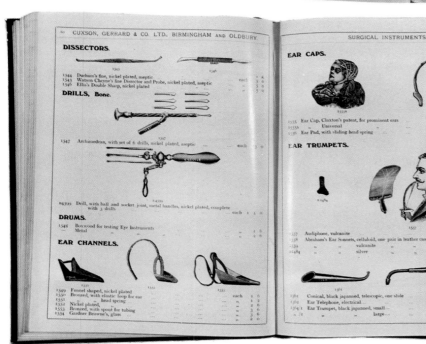

Right

Doulton & Co. Ltd. Sanitary Ware Catalogue, Vulcanware Slop Sinks, 1912.
(Yesterday's Paper) £6

Cuxson, Gerrard & Co. Ltd., catalogue for medical and hospital supplies, circa 1910.
(Yesterday's Paper) £45

Alfred Goslett & Co. Ltd. stained glass window catalogue, 1890's.
(Yesterday's Paper) £15

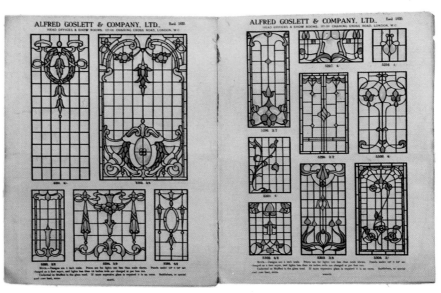

Trade Catalogues

Trade Catalogues

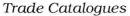

Left

Huntley & Palmers Biscuits
catalogue, 1930's.
(Yesterday's Paper)   £35

Consul Brochure, 1961.
(Yesterday's Paper)   £5

**Architectural Door & Window
Fittings** trade catalogue of
Parker, Winder & Achurch Ltd.,
Birmingham, 11¹/₂in. high.
(Sam Weller)   £20

Right

Meccano Toys of Quality
Catalogue, 1956.
(Yesterday's Paper)   £5

**Good Furniture for the
Modern Home**, 1930's,
catalogue from Sidebottoms of
York.
(Yesterday's Paper)   £6

Corset catalogue, 1950's,
'Every Woman's Problem'.
(Yesterday's Paper)   £6

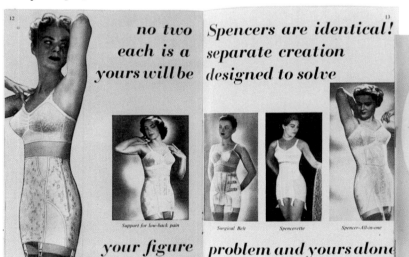

Trade Catalogues

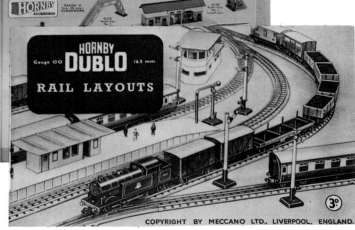

Fortnum & Mason Christmas Gift catalogue, 1966.
(Yesterday's Paper)   £3

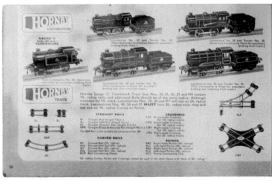

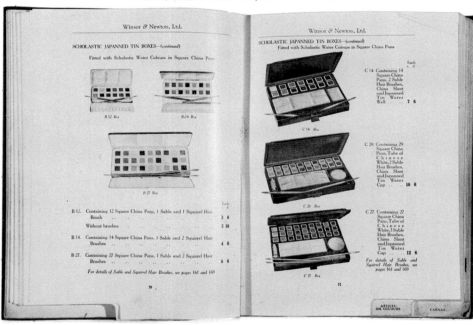

Hornby Dublo Rail Layouts catalogue, 1956.
(Yesterday's Paper)   £8

Winsor & Newton Ltd, general catalogue for artists' requisites, 1934.
(Yesterday's Paper)   £15

Trade Catalogues

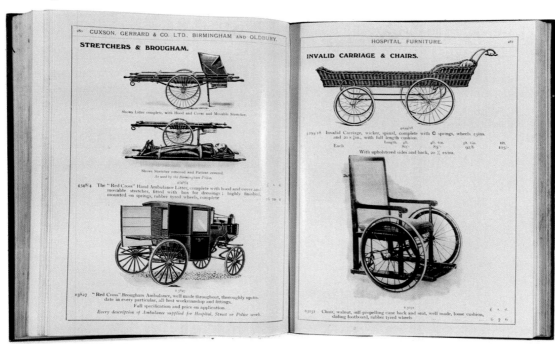

Cuxson, Gerrard & Co Ltd., catalogue for medical and hospital supplies, circa 1910.
(Yesterday's Paper)   £45

Catalogue for **Toilet Services** by Smith & Ford, 1880's.
(Dave Lewis)   £300

Trade Catalogue for **Stewart-Warner radios,** 1920's.
(Yesterday's Paper)   £6

Trade Catalogues

Cement Marketing Company catalogue, 'Artistic Concrete', 1932. (Yesterday's Paper) £8

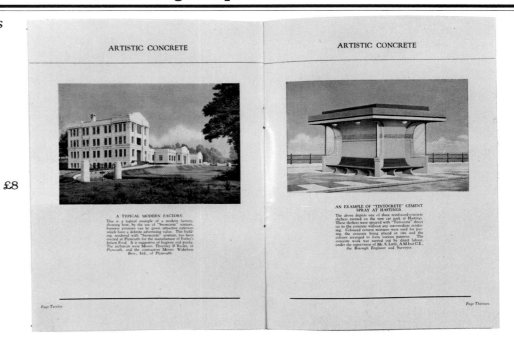

William Perring furniture catalogue, 1930's (Yesterday's Paper) £5

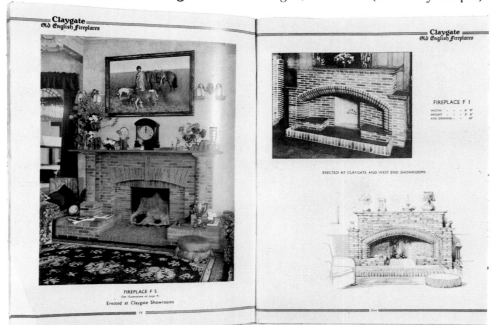

Claygate 'Old English Fireplaces', catalogue, 1930's. (Yesterday's Paper) £6

Trade Catalogues

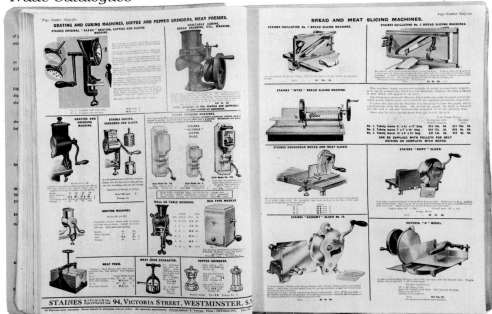

Staines Kitchen Equipment Co. Ltd, catalogue for June 1932. (Yesterday's Paper)   £15

Morris Oxford Brochure, 1962.   (Yesterday's Paper)   £5

Hirst Bros. of Manchester, clock catalogue, 1910. (Yesterday's Paper)   £30

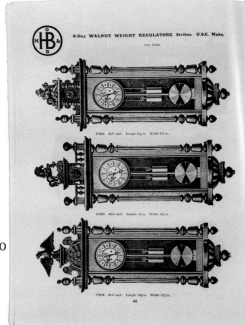
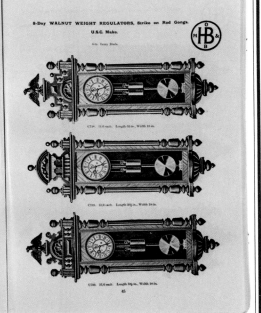

Trays

Trays were another advertising gimmick, given away free to publicans by brewers and distillers from the mid 1880s onwards. This is one field where the ubiquitous plastic has never replaced metal as the favoured material, though impressed bakelite enjoyed a short vogue in the 1930s.

Wrights Biscuits tin tray with **Mabel Lucie Attwell** design.
(Muir Hewitt)   £25
Watson's No 10 Scotch change tray by Shelley, 5in. wide.
(Dave Lewis)   £40
Edwardian **Schweppes Soda Water, Schweppes Dry Ginger Ale**, printed tin tray, 13in. diameter.
(Dave Lewis)   £50
1950's **Guinness Extra Stout**, printed tin tray, **'Opening Time is Guinness Time'**, 10in. diameter.
(Dave Lewis)   £10
Edwardian printed tin tray for **Marshalls Semolina, Pure, Dainty & Nourishing Wheaten Foods**.
(Dave Lewis)   £35

Trays

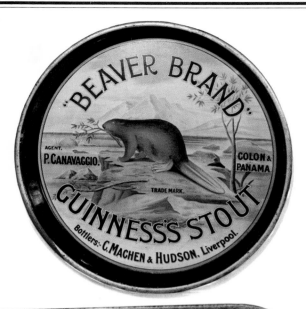

Daniel Crawfords Scotch Whisky, printed tin tray.
(Dave Lewis)   £35
Beaver Brand Guinness's Stout pictorial tin tray made by Woollen & Co., Sheffield, 12in. diameter.
(Dave Lewis)   £45
The Jubilee tea pot stand, Queen Victoria.
(Cyril Wickham)   £50
Edwardian printed tin tray for **Marshalls Farola, Delicious puddings, custards, shapes**.
(Dave Lewis)   £45
Printed tin tray, **'You are quite right, WORTHINGTON is the best'**, 12in. diameter.
(Dave Lewis)   £45